ROBERTS, David.
The Holy Land, Syria, Idumea, Arabia, Egypt and Nubia From Drawings made on the Spot…with historical Descriptions by the Rev. George Croly [and] William Brockendon. London, F.G. Moon, 1842-1849.

the Exotic and the Beautiful

With warmest wishes from all of us at

Making More Possible

the Exotic and the Beautiful
the world in colour

THE COLLECTION OF COLOUR PLATE BOOKS
FROM THE LIBRARY OF NORMAN R. BOBINS

VOLUME I

The Americas, the Indies, Arctica, Africa, Levant, Imperial Russia,
the Indian Subcontinent, the Far East and Pacifica

Christine Thomson

COUNTRYWIDE
EDITIONS

PUBLISHED BY
Countrywide Editions Ltd

IN ASSOCIATION WITH
BERNARD *j* SHAPERO
RARE BOOKS

Published by Countrywide Editions 2005

Photography: Michael Tropea

First published in Great Britain in 2005 by
Countrywide Editions Ltd
24 Maddox Street
London
W1S 1PP

A CIP catalogue record for this book is available from the British Library

ISBN 0 9551701 0 9
ISBN 978 0 9551701 0 2

Printed and bound in Great Britain by Raithby, Lawrence

time was to apply a non-biological theory of civilisation to non-European people; "the inherent humanity of the savage was tender and sensitive with a kind regard for his fellow man".

To revert to Europe, the idea of the "Sublime" was also important to the traveller in the eighteenth century. They were able to ignore the rigours of the roads in their headlong search across Europe for beauty and sublimity, whether natural or artistic. Waterways were the domain of the Low Countries, but to avoid Germany's roads, considered the worst in Europe, water became an alternative. A boat up the Rhine, with its romantic castles, towns and cities, then became another of the Grand Tour destinations. The mountains and glaciers of Switzerland were also declared "sublime" by George Keate, and that country's popularity was secured. Keate was guided by Saussure, botanist, geologist and mountaineer of some note. Such sights became of increasing interest in the second part of the eighteenth century, greater concern being given to natural phenomena.

Impossible to itemise all the beauties and wonders of this collection – hot air balloons, railways, bridges, dams under construction, as well the most magnificent cityscapes, landscapes and waterscapes and remarkable costume plates of a great variety of countries worldwide – we must refer the reader of this catalogue to the illustrations which we hope will speak for themselves. One of Mr. Bobins' particular interests is sporting books. Although we have allocated the most important sporting works to the relevant countries, for instance the very rare and beautiful Hungarian edition of Andrasy's work on Hungarian hunting and Williamson's Oriental Field Sports to Indian Subcontinent, we have devoted a section to sporting pursuits in America and Great Britain at the end of Vol. II. His other particular interest, military costumes, we have handled in the same way, with a special section at the beginning of that volume. This should be considered a unique collection in breadth and quality.

Christine Thomson
London, October 2005

WA-PEL-LA

CHIEF OF THE MUSQUAKEES.

PUBLISHED BY F. W. GREENOUGH, PHILAD.ᵃ

Drawn Printed & Coloured at I.T. Bowen's Lithographic Establishment Nº 94 Walnut St.

Entered according to act of Congress in the Year 1838 by F. Greenough, in the Clerks Office of the District Court of the Eastern District of Pennᵃ

Contents

ONE
South America and West Indies | 12

TWO
North America, Canada and Arctica | 40

THREE
Africa, Atlantic and Canary Islands | 78

FOUR
Levant and Ottoman Empire | 120

FIVE
Imperial Russia | 166

SIX
Indian Subcontinent | 184

SEVEN
East Indies and Far East | 232

EIGHT
Pacific including Antipodes | 262

Imp Lemercier Paris

LA LECHERA

South America
and West Indies

BELISARIO, I.M.
Sketches of Character, An Illustration of the Habits, Occupation, and Costume of the Negro Population in the Island of Jamaica.
Kingston, Jamaica, by the Artist at his Residence, London, and sold by Messrs. Jas. Wallace & Co., Messrs. Smith & Clark; Messrs. Jordon & Osborn; L. Treadway; Wm. Carver, and F. Egan, 1837-38.

3 original parts, folio, 12 handcoloured lithographed plates by A. Duperly, loose as issued in original wrappers, preserved in modern black morocco box. Single gilt fillets, corner pieces, spine gilt in compartments, raised bands.
Abbey Travel II, 685; Colas 279; Cundall, Bibl. Jamaicensis, 294.

Colas erroneously says that only eight plates were published. Although twelve parts were promised in the first part, no trace can be found that more than three were ever produced. Abbey suggests that it was obvious from the last part that the artist was finding it difficult to get fresh material and it was clear that there was petering out of support for the book. While the first part is more often found and had a subscription list of 165 names, the second part is more rare and the third part almost never seen. Abbey suggests that the promise at the end of the first subscription list to repeat it at the end of the work together with names of subsequent subscribers, is a good example of an attempt to make use of the stimulus of social conformity inherent in a subscription list, a stimulus especially effective in a small community as was Jamaica.

The plates are mainly costume plates and include some Jamaican trades chimneysweeper, milk-woman, water-jar sellers and several connected with the band of the Jaw-Bone and the House John-Canoe.

BENTLEY, Charles [and] SCHOMBURGK, Robert Hermann.
Twelve Views in the Interior of Guiana from drawings executed by Mr Charles Bentley, after Sketches taken during the Expedition carried out in the Years 1835 and 1839, under the direction of the Royal Geographical Society of London, and aided by Her Majesty's Government…
London, Ackermann and Co., 1841.

Folio, lithographed pictorial title, map of Guiana (John Murray) and 12 tinted lithographed plates by C. Hullmandel after Bentley, and lithographed by G. Barnard, Coke Smith, P. Gauci, with accompanying text by Schomburgk, all handcoloured, wood-engraved illustrations in text, title laid down on upper cover of later green cloth gilt binding.
Abbey Travel 720; Cundall, West Indies No. 1542; Sabin 77796; Tooley (1954) No. 447.

Schomburgk, who wrote the text of this work, in a subsequent expedition was to lay down the Schomburgk line dividing British Guyana from Venezuela.

BONAFFE, A.A.
Reguerdos de Lima, Album de Tipos, Trajes y Costumbres Dibujados y Publicados …
Lima and Paris, 1857.

2 vols., large folio, Vol. II slightly smaller, 12 lithographed plates after Moranie and lithographed by Prugue, plates partially coloured by hand, French translation in each lower margin, original blue pebbled cloth, bordered in blind enclosing gilt lettering direct.
G.e. Palau, p. 246; Hiler p. 101; not in Colas or Lipperheide.

Also in this collection is another edition of 1857 with an entirely different set of plates from this earlier edition.

CADDY, Lieut. J.G.
Scenery of the Windward & Leeward Island.
London, Ackermann & Co., 1837 (watermarked J. Whatman Turkey Mill 1850).

Oblong folio, 12 handcoloured aquatint plates by J. Harris, Newton Fielding, William Westall, C. Hunt, all after Caddy, on India proof paper mounted on Whatman paper, paper printed on was very fine and quite fragile, issued loose in an original folder, gilt lettered within gilt scroll panel: Scenery of the Windward & Leeward Islands etc. each plate was signed Drawn by Lieut. Caddy, Royal Artillery; engraver's name given; imprint: Ackermann etc., without text as issued, loose in 19th century green cloth portfolio, gilt lettered within border on upper cover, ties.
Abbey Travel II, 692; Sabin III, 9824.

Very rare complete set of these attractive views. Little is known of the artist, bar that he was of the Royal Engineers.

CASTRO, Casimiro, artist [and] GARCIA CUBAS, Antonio.
Album del Ferro-Carril Mexicano... Mexico, Victor Debray & Co., 1877.

Large folio, 25 chromolithographed plates by A. Sigogne after Castro, including title, double page lithographed map, loose as issued in original pictorial board folder, cloth backed, ties, preserved in modern green linen covered folder and slipcase.
Mathes, Mexico on Stone, p. 42; Palau 98733.

A magnificent series of chromolithographs showing the Mexican railway, crossing bridges through the rain forests. Spain's possessions in the New World had gradually been adapting to the scientific revolution of the late 17th and 18th century in Europe, coming under the influence of French political and scientific concepts. With a Valois King on the Spanish throne, these filtered through to the New World, and foreign visitors arrived, opening an area which had been isolated from other nations for two centuries. The art of lithography was adopted and developed in Mexico after Sennefelder's famous publication on the subject in Germany which was universally influential. This art became a symbol of national pride and prestige as did new Mexican urban architecture and systems of transport, see this work with two new developments combined.

CASTRO, J.; CAMPILLO, J; BUDA, L; RODRIGUEZ, G.
Mexico y sus Alrededores. Colleccion de monumentos, trajes y paisajes...
Mexico, Decaen 1855-56 [58].

Large folio, 45 on 41 lithographed plates, lithographed title, folding plan, all plates with titles in English, Spanish and French and all but plates 1 & 2 titled Mexico y sus Alrededores, the plan is of Mexico city and printed in black, three colours and a background tint, half red morocco over red decorated cloth, gilt borders, spine raised bands, ruled in black and red, gilt in compartments, gilt lettered a direct.
Abbey Travel 672; Colas 547; Lipperheide 1624; Sabin 485;9; Mathes, Mexico on Stone, pp. 28-29 and 57. Toussaint, La Litografia en Mexico, p. xviii.

This collection contains a second copy of 1869 with 40 handcoloured lithographs on 36 plates printed by V. Debray, Mexico y Sus Alredores. All the bibliographies quoted are for the 1855-6 edition. The plan of Mexico city was added in 1858. Thirty plates were initially produced with the remaining appearing in 1857. Abbey comments that the draughtsmanship and lithography were of a very high standard.

European explorers La Perouse 1782; Malaspina 1792 and Alexander von Humboldt, 1803 along with Mexican savants found new fascination in flora; geography and archaeological antiquities of New Spain and Mexican countryside. There was a strong sense of nationalism in Mexico and with it interest in pre-Columbian heritage, love of Mexican dress, customs and landscape. "To the foreigner Mexico was mysterious and ancient. To the Mexican mysterious and majestic" (Mathes). Decaen was one of the foremost exponents. This was considered one of the most significant lithographic productions in the history of art. The most important work illustrating Mexico City in the 19th century (Mathes).

06

VIEW OF THE CITY OF RIO DE JANEIRO TAKEN FROM THE ANCHORAGE.

68

CATHERWOOD, Frederick.
Views of Ancient Monuments in Central America Chiapas and Yucatan.
London, F. Catherwood, 1844.

Large folio, chromolithographed title by Owen Jones, dedication, 24pp., 26 handcoloured lithographed plates mounted on 25 cards after sketches by the author, preserved in a green morocco backed cloth box, spine gilt lettered within decorative gilt frame, text in original yellow wrappers.
Sabin 11520; Palau 50290; Tooley 133.

Only 300 copies were printed. The letterpress is by John Stephens with whom Catherwood travelled throughout the region described, starting in 1839. In a real sense they were the people who rediscovered the glories of the Mayan civilisation which had remained hidden, overgrown by jungle, for a thousand years. Catherwood's illustrations convey the beauty and mystery of these forgotten treasures as well as combining the earliest depictions in modern times (Sabin).

CHAMBERLAIN, Lieut. Henry.
Views and Costumes of the City and Neighbourhood of Rio de Janeiro, Brazil.
London, printed for Thomas M'Lean by Howlett and Brimmer, Columbian Press, 1822.

Folio, with address list and list of plates, 36 handcoloured aquatint plates, including 5 folding panoramic views, by T. Hunt, G. Hunt, H. Alden, and John Clark after drawings by Chamberlain, contemporary blue morocco, triple gilt fillet, spine gilt in compartments, raised bands, morocco label, g.e., inner ruled gilt dentelle, slightly later marbled endpapers. From the Bradford/Weston Library.
Borba de Moraes p. 178; Tooley 136; Abbey Travel 707.

Extremely rare, fine First Edition of "one of the most beautiful, and also one of the rarest, books published on Brazil in the nineteenth century" (Borba de Moraes). Identified by Tooley as "the finest English colour plate book on Brazil", this work contains harbour views, landscapes, sociological and architectural scenes drawn by Chamberlain from 1819-1820. Abbey suggest that Chamberlain was probably the son of Sir Henry Chamberlain who held the posts of Consul-General and Charge d'Affaires in Rio de Janeiro from 1815 to 1829. Originally issued in parts.

CLARK, William.
Ten Views in the Island of Antigua.
London, Thomas Clay, 1823.

First edition. Oblong folio, 10 unsigned handcoloured aquatints, on Whatman paper, 4 plates slightly trimmed so watermark not visible, each plate with accompanying text, slightly later half morocco, spine flat and gilt banded, red morocco titling label on upper cover.
Abbey Travel 690; Tooley 147; Cundall, Bibliography of the West Indies 222.

Rare work on Antigua, beautifully illustrated. Clark spent three years in the West Indies upon the estates of Admiral Tallemach. While there he made drawings of the process of sugar making, showing workers on a number of estates, "in the field, boiling-house and distillery".

09

DEBRET, Jean Baptiste.
Voyage Pittoresque et Historique au Brasil depuis 1816
jusqu'en 1833.
Paris, Firmin Didot Freres, 1833.

3 vols., folio, engraved frontispiece portrait of the author, 153
handcoloured lithographs on 140 leaves by C. Motte after
Debret, and three maps, [prospectus], contemporary morocco
backed boards.
Sabin 19122; Borba de Moraes p. 214.

Debret was writing at the time of the regeneration of
Brazil, and mentions the abdication of S.M.D. Pedro of
the Brazilian Empire. Sabin describes this as a "good
work" and remarks that there are coloured copies as here.
The work was produced in 24 original parts, during the
years 1834 to 1839. Debret's work had a very slow start.
The work initially did not sell well. It seems that a large
part, unbound, remained in storage for decades. However
suddenly in the 1930s it took off, prices rose and the
Brazilian people discovered it. A street in the centre of
Rio de Janeiro was named after Debret and his plates
when framed provided decoration. His Voyage
Pittoresque, became a la mode and copies became scarce.
(Borba de Moraes.)

DUPERREY, Louis.
Voyage autour du monde, execute par Ordre du Roi, sur…la Coquille.
Paris, 1826.

Histoire naturelle Zoologie 2 vols. plus Atlas Hydrographique. Together 3 vols., 4to and folio, 157 aquatint and lithographed plates, mostly handcoloured, contemporary morocco backed cloth.
Sabin 21353; Hill p. 90.

The author led a French Government expedition to the Pacific area on board the Coquille. During the voyage they visited Brazil, the Falkland Islands, Australia, New Zealand, Java, Mauritius and many Pacific Islands including Tahiti and Tonga. Vast quantities of ethnographic and scientific data were collected. The remarkable plates include portraits, dramatic landscapes and scenes of village life.

HENDERSON, James.
A History of Brazil: comprising its Geography, Commerce, Colonization, Aboriginal Inhabitants…
London, for the author, 1821.

First edition. 4to, preliminaries, 522pp. text, 28 handcoloured lithographed plates, including frontispiece, by C. Shoesmith after James Henderson, printed by Hullmandel, two folding maps, one of Brazil lithographed by B.R. Baker and printed by Hullmandel, this coloured, the second Mapa da Comarca do Sabara executed by the same as above; now bound without list of subscribers, watermarked J. Whatman and J. Whatman 1821. (Abbey in fact refers to watermarks from 1818, 1819 and 1820.) Borba de Moraes, pp. 334-35; Abbey Travel II, 706; Sabin 31314.

Henderson studied Brazil during a failed visit to obtain a position at the British Legation in Rio; unsuccessful in this aspiration, he was received into the house of a merchant and the knowledge of South America he gained was sufficient for him to be appointed Consul General for Columbia in Bogota. The views in this work are made from his own drawings on the spot and represent an important visual documentation of Brazilian history. Abbey describes these early lithographs of poor quality. However, the work had 480 subscribers. One of the plates shows a sugar plantation and the owner's house. Other plates show costumes, others trades of pedler, miner, and also a view of Rio de Janeiro. Hullmandel printed the majority of the plates. He had studied under Faraday in order to understand the chemical basis of lithography and wrote in his Art of Drawing on Stone, 1824, that he considered that early English lithographers were superior in landscape work, while the French printers excelled at portraiture. It seems likely that it was Hullmandel who persuaded Ackermann to publish the translation of Senefelder's Vollstaendiges Lehrbuch in 1819 and he also had a hand in persuading the Royal Society of Arts to present a Gold Medal to Senefelder (the pioneer of lithographic art), although it was Ackermann who communicated with the Society and presented them with a Portable Lithographic Press and other material. Ackermann realised the financial benefits of lithography with its possibility of longer print runs at a reduced price to meet increasing demand. Possibly because the new art in its early stages was too different in quality from the delicate aquatints his own customers were accustomed to, he transferred his lithographic work to Hullmandel's establishment (Abbey).

13

¹³

HAKEWILL, James.
A Picturesque Tour of the Island of Jamaica…
London, Hurst and Robinson; E. Lloyd, 1825.

Folio, 21 handcoloured aquatint plates, some slightly heightened with gum Arabic, with accompanying preliminary text and short descriptive text, late 19th/early 20th century red morocco, double gilt fillet, spine with raised bands, gilt in compartments, g.e., inner gilt dentelle.
Abbey Travel 683; Tooley 240; Sabin 29591; Prideaux pp. 255, 338.

The work was originally published in 7 original parts. Abbey states that a book which was possibly a version of the above was published by Lloyd in 1827. Each part was sold at 15s and according to the wrapper for Part 5, the parts were also on sale in America at $3 each. (This copy is watermarked Turkey Mill 1823.) The leaf relating to the conditions of the Negroes at the beginning of Part 2 is very rare. It is slightly smaller than the rest of the work, and is on different paper. It begins by saying that the author had intended to give all his information about the Negroes in the general history at the end of the work, but the particular circumstances of the time induced him to anticipate that design… The information is in fact repeated at the beginning of the Introduction in Part 7.

¹⁴

[JOHNSON, J.]
An Historical and Descriptive Account of Antigua, illustrated by numerous engravings, coloured in imitation of drawings taken on the spot, accompanied by a map of the islands… with a list of proprietors, number of slaves, &c &c and a chronological table of events connected with the colony.
London, Henry Baylis for the author, 1830.

Oblong folio, errata slip, advertisement slip , half title, handcoloured engraved map by J.& H. Neele after Johnson, in sections linen backed, 7 fine handcoloured aquatint plates, all after Johnson, by C. Bentley, G. Reeve, T. Fielding, E. Duncan, one unsigned, half straight grained wine morocco blindstamped and gilt ruled, label laid down on upper cover, new endpapers.
This work not in Abbey or Tooley.

Very rare, before the Keynes copy at Christies, the last to have been apparently sold at auction was in March 1925. Johnson's original plan was to publish a large series of Views in the West Indies with each part containing images and descriptions of a number of islands. This plan seems to have been abandoned after only three parts because objections were made to the form in which these West Indian views were published. Apparently purchasers wanted to be able to buy views of individual islands. This work includes amended versions of six of the views which had previously appeared in the views in the West Indies and one additional view not published before, the only such offshoot of the original to appear as far as can be seen. There was apparently difficulty in finding subscribers. A depressed Johnson wrote that so few people had come forward that he was not sure if it was even worth printing the list of subscribers.

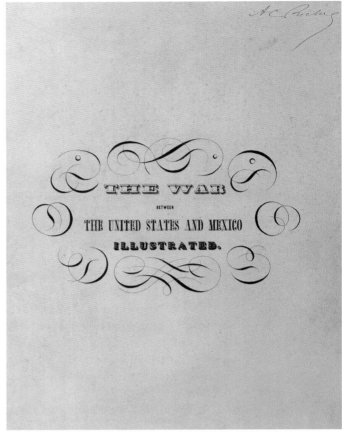

15

16

KENDALL, George Wilkins [and] NEBEL, Carl.
The War between the United States and Mexico Illustrated, Embracing Pictorial Drawings of all the Principal Conflicts.
New York and Philadelphia, D. and George Appleton, 1851.

2 vols., folio and oblong folio atlas of 12 coloured lithographed plates by Bayot after drawings by Carl Nebel, printed on card by Lemercier of Paris, loose in the original portfolio, text in original printed wrappers, the whole preserved in green morocco backed, gilt ruled, upper cover with ornate gilt cartouche, gilt lettered, ties.
Howes K76; Sabin 37362; Bennett.

The best pictorial record of the war with Mexico. Kendall, a journalist with the New Orleans Picayune, had repeatedly endorsed U.S. military action against Mexico. When war broke out he "rode with the rangers, witnessed most of Taylor's battles, and himself captured a cavalry flag... he attached himself as a voluntary aide to the staff of General Worth and saw nearly all the fighting from Vera Cruz to Chapultepec. He was mentioned in dispatches and wounded in the knee in the storming of the last fortress" (DAB). The plates were produced in Paris and the text printed in New Orleans, the book being bound and sold by Appleton in New York.

KOSTER, Henry.
Travels in Brazil...
London, For Longman, Hurst, Rees, Orme, and Brown, 1816.

4to, preliminaries, references to the plan, text 501pp., 8 handcoloured aquatint plates, engraved map of Pernambuco and a plan of the Port of Pernambuco, both uncoloured, 3ll, publisher's advertisements inserted at the beginning of the work, contemporary calf gilt.
Abbey Travel 704; Prideaux pp. 255, 342; Sabin, No. 38272.

The plates which are unsigned show a planter and his wife on a journey; a Jangada; crossing a river; a Sertanejo; fishing canoe; lady going to visit; a cotton carrier and a sugar mill. A second edition in 2 vols., 8vo was published in 1817; an American edition was published in Philadelphia 1817; a French edition, Paris, 1818; and a German edition, Weimar, 1827.

LEIGHTON, R.A.
Five Views in Baptist Chapels in Jamaica.
London, R. Cartwright, 1840.

Folio, 5 handcoloured lithographed plates, original wrappers preserved in modern green cloth portfolio.
Not in Abbey or Tooley, NUC or BLC.

An attractive set of plates on an interesting subject. Extremely rare.

LINATI, C.
Costumes Civils, Militaries et Religieux du Mexique.
Brussels, Lithographie Royale de Jobard, [1828].

4to, 24 unn. pp. descriptive text, 48 handcoloured lithographed plates no. 1-48 drawn by Linati, plus title, published in 12 original parts each with four plates, original pink wrappers dated 1828, contemporary calf backed marbled boards, sometime re-cornered, preserved in modern cloth covered box.
Colas 1872; Lipperheide 1622; Palau 138502; Vinet 2232.

An edition appeared in London in 1830 lithographed in colours by Engelmann.

MAWE, John.
Travels in the Interior of Brasil.
London, by M'Dowall for Longman, Hurst, Rees, Orme and Brown, and sold by the Author, 1823.

Second edition. 8vo, 5 handcoloured plates, one engraved, four aquatinted, uncoloured engraved map.
Abbey Travel 709 refers to 1825 edition and other editions including 1823; Borba de Moraes II, p. 543; Sabin 21271.

After a difficult period, imprisoned as an English spy in Montevideo in 1805, Mawe obtained his liberty but subsequently being interned until the capture of Montevideo by General Beresford in 1806. He accompanied General Whitelocke's expedition to Buenos Aires, and on his return to Montevideo purchased a schooner and sailed to Brazil, putting in at various ports on the way. He was well received in Brazil by the Prince Regent, Dom Pedro, who gave him permission to visit the diamond mines of Minas Geraes and other parts of the interior during 1809-10, and also granted him access to the government archives. On his return to England he became well known as a practical mineralogist.

MAY, B.
Album Pintoresco de la Isla de Cuba.[Havana].
n.p., n.d. [c.1855].

Oblong 4to, chromolithographed pictorial title, folding lithographed plan within border of tinted lithographed vignettes, folding lithographed map within similar border and 26 mostly tinted lithographed plates, original red cloth decorated in blind and gilt.

The maps and plates are mainly of Havana.

21

[MEXICO.]
Album Pintoresco de la Republica Mexicana.
Mexico, Julio Michaud y Thomas, [c. 1850].

Oblong folio, 24 lithographed plates, four handcoloured and
heightened with gum Arabic, remaining 20, tinted lithographs,
all by Pedro Federico Lehnert (artist).
Not in Abbey.

An apparently scarce piece of Mexican lithography, at an
important time for the art in Mexico.

22

MEYER, Dr Hans.
In the High Andes of Ecuador: Chimborazo, Cotopaxi, etc
(In den Hoch-Anden von Ecuador, Bilder Atlas).
[Berlin], 1908.

Folio (atlas volume), 23 chromolithographed plates, of which one
double-page, and 40 collotype views on 20 plates after Rudolf
Reschreiter, 11 handcoloured tinted lithographed plates,
numbered at upper right corner, this latter in red boards, plates
mounted and captioned on card, photographic illustrations also
on card, 8vo text vol. (dated 1907), the whole preserved in
original red card folder.

An interesting and uncommon work. One auction record
only. Shows magnificent and normally inaccessible views
of the Ecuadorian High Andes.

PORTER, Lieut. Whitworth and Mrs. Porter.
Views of the Island of Dominica. n.p. 1849.

Small folio, title, dedication 11 handcoloured tinted lithographed
plates, original publisher's blue wrappers, with lithographed
titling, preserved in modern maroon cloth slip case.
Abbey Travel 695; Sabin 64193; Cundall, West Indies, 179.

Charming set of views of Dominica, probably according to
Abbey published for private circulation. The plates include
views of Roseau, Government House, Prince Rupert's Bay
and Morne Daniole. In the dedication to the Governor of
Dominica, Porter stated he had wanted to demonstrate the
"beauty and grandeur" of the island and to choose "the
most familiar views", "considered the most likely to be
interesting to the inhabitants". Cundall's 179 is obviously
this work, although he dates it 1840, possibly in error. He
gives Lieut. Porter's first name as "Whiteworth".

24

REICHEL, Levin Theodor.
Bilder aus Westindien.
Berlin, L. Kraatz, 1861.

5 parts, small oblong folio, 10 colour lithographed plates, two parts in original wrappers, plates loose as issued with descriptive text, preserved in modern green cloth portfolio, spine with printed label.

25

SCHMIDTMEYER, Peter.
Travels into Chile, Over the Andes, in the Years 1820 and 1821.
London, Longman, Hurst, Rees, 1824.

4to, 2 folding lithographed plans, 26 lithographed plates, including 18 handcoloured (Abbey records only 9 as handcoloured), and one folding by G. Scharf and A. Aglio after Schmidtmeyer and General J. Paroissien.
Abbey Travel II, 715; Sabin 77692.

Schmidtmeyer's work, previously published in Paris, contains "sketches of the productions and agriculture; mines and metallurgy; inhabitants, history, and other features of America; particularly of Chile and Arauco".

A

TWO YEARS' CRUISE

OFF

TIERRA DEL FUEGO,

THE FALKLAND ISLANDS,

PATAGONIA,

AND IN

THE RIVER PLATE:

𝔄 𝔑𝔞𝔯𝔯𝔞𝔱𝔦𝔳𝔢 𝔬𝔣 𝔏𝔦𝔣𝔢 𝔦𝔫 𝔱𝔥𝔢 𝔖𝔬𝔲𝔱𝔥𝔢𝔯𝔫 𝔖𝔢𝔞𝔰.

BY

W. PARKER SNOW,

LATE COMMANDER OF THE MISSION YACHT
"ALLEN GARDINER;"
Author of "Voyage of the *Prince Albert* in search of Sir John Franklin."

WITH CHARTS AND ILLUSTRATIONS.

IN TWO VOLUMES.

VOL. I.

LONDON:
LONGMAN, BROWN, GREEN, LONGMANS, & ROBERTS.
1857.

26

26

SNOW, W. Parker.
A Two Years' Cruise off Tierra del Fuego, The Falkland Islands, Patagonia, and in the River Plate.
London, Longman, Brown, 1857.

First edition. 2 vols., 8vo, 6 chromolithographed plates, 3 hand-tinted folding maps.
Sabin 85559.

On his voyage South Snow commanded the Mission Yacht Allen Gardiner, named for the naval commander who founded the Patagonian Missionary Society in 1844. Gardiner and his crew landed in Tierra del Fuego to found their mission, but took ill and died before help could reach them. Snow then established the mission headquarters on Keppel Island, South Falklands in 1855 at a period when the mission was battling against sealers and whalers, for reducing and mistreating the wild life. Included are his remarks on the Falklands as a penal settlement, proposed by Governor Moore and supported by Snow. Attached is the folio "Blue Book" of proceedings in the House of Commons in 1858, where Snow put his case against his removal as the master of the Allen Gardiner by the Governor. The Governor had detained the vessel just as Snow was about to put to sea.

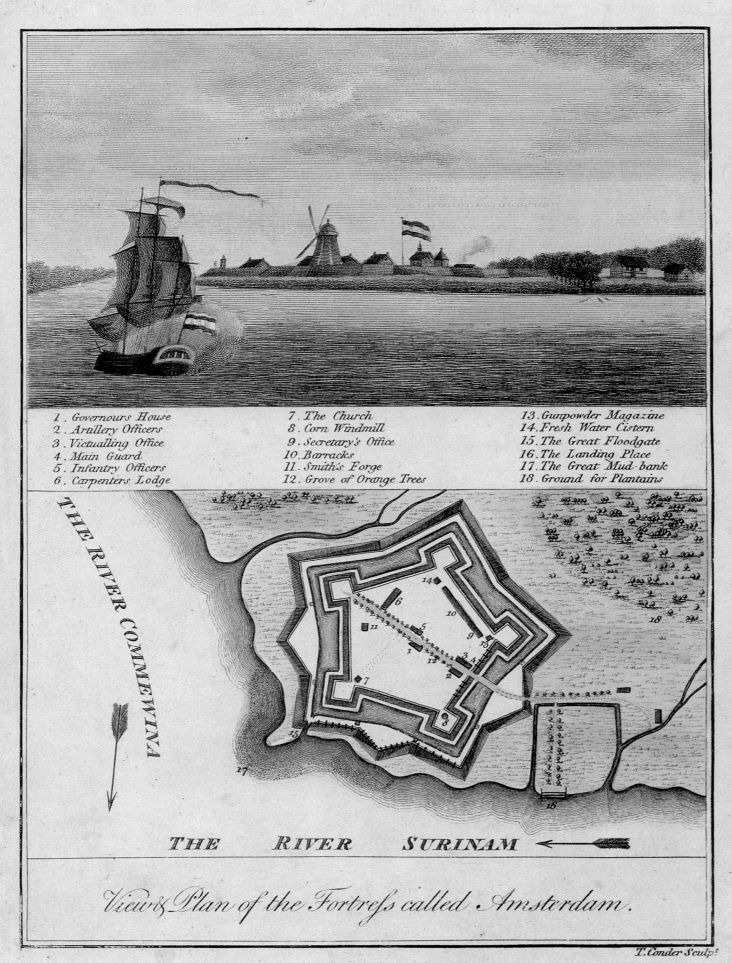

1. Governours House
2. Artillery Officers
3. Victualling Office
4. Main Guard
5. Infantry Officers
6. Carpenters Lodge

7. The Church
8. Corn Windmill
9. Secretary's Office
10. Barracks
11. Smith's Forge
12. Grove of Orange Trees

13. Gunpowder Magazine
14. Fresh Water Cistern
15. The Great Floodgate
16. The Landing Place
17. The Great Mud-bank
18. Ground for Plantains

THE RIVER COMMEWINA

THE RIVER SURINAM

View & Plan of the Fortress called Amsterdam.

T. Conder Sculp!

London, Published Dec.r 1st 1791, by J. Johnson, St Pauls Church Yard.

14

STEDMAN, Capt. John Gabriel.
Narrative for a Five Years' Expedition against the Revolted Negroes of Surinam, in Guiana.
London, for J. Johnson, 1806.

Second edition. 2 vols., 4to, dedication, preface, subscriber's list, contents, text pp. 1-14, 15-30, *29, *30 to 407, 81 engraved plates, large paper and with all the plates handcoloured, contemporary sprinkled calf, spine raised bands, gilt ruled in compartments.
Abbey Travel 719; Cardinall 622 (for 1813 edition); Cox, II, pg. 285; Cundall, West Indies, 1715; Sabin 91075.

This large paper copy cost £7.7s on publication as opposed to the ordinary uncoloured copy which cost £5.5s. The number of additions, abridgements, translations and versions which were published shows the impact made at the time by Stedman's unaffected Narrative of his experiences in Guiana. According to the Dictionary of National Biography, William Thomson edited the work. Many of the plates, it will be noticed, were engraved by Blake, who had learnt his trade from Basire, to whom he was apprenticed for seven years from August 1772. Keynes reported in his William Blake's Engravings, 1950, that from 1791 until 1800 Blake did much work as a journeyman engraver for the booksellers. Stedman, an officer in the Scots Brigade in Holland, volunteered for service against the Negroes in Dutch Guiana. While out there he to all intents married the subject of plate number 9, Joanna a Mulatto, and had a son by her, who became a midshipman in the British Navy, but died young. The author emerges as a most interesting and sympathetic character. (Abbey). Blake engraved 13 plates, while three were engraved by Bartolozzi.

STEINMANN, J.
Souvenirs de Rio de Janeiro, dessins d'apres Nature…
Basle, J. Steinmann, 1835.

First edition. Oblong folio, 12 handcoloured lithographed plates, original illustrated wrappers with added gouache by Salathe within a black border after drawings by the author (9), Kretschman (2), and Barrat (1), each mounted on buff card as issued, tissue guards, title to upper wrapper surrounded by pictorial vignettes, without text as issued, preserved in modern morocco backed cloth box.
Borba de Noraes p. 286.

Steinmann, born in Switzerland, introduced the art of lithography into Brazil. He travelled to Rio de Janeiro in 1825, under contract to the Military Archive, where he lectured until 1830. He had a workshop at the Rua do Ouvidor 119, and at the Rua da Ajuda, where he produced many plates, working for, amongst others, the Tipografia Imperial and Nacional. It seems that Steinmann put copies of his album for sale in Paris, Chez Rittner et Goupil. All bookdealers who bought it could print their own names on the cover where a space had been left for the purpose (trouver chez…). The plates, which are vivid, provide a superb record of the city and are as follows: Ilha das Cobras; Moro do Castello & de Pray d'Ajuda; Vista do Sacco d'Alfers & de St. Cristovao; Novo Friburgo (Colonia Suissa), do Morro Queimado; Planta de Caf; Bota Fogo; Igreja de St. Sebastian; Largo do Pao; St. Joao de Carachy, a Praya Grande; Vista Tomada de St. Thereza; Vista de N.S. da Gloria et da Barra do Rio de Janeiro; Caminho dos Orgas.

TEMSKY, G.F. von. Mitla.
A Narrative of Incidents and Personal Adventures on a
Journey in Mexico, Guatamala and Salvador, 1853 to 1855.
With Observations on the Modes of Life in those Countries.
London, Longman, Brown, Green, Longmans, & Roberts,
1858.

8vo, 14 plates, of which five are chromolithographed (nos. 1,
3, 4, 6, 11), 9 other plates, uncoloured wood-engravings,
coloured folding map of route through Mexico, Guatamala &
S. Salvador, contemporary calf gilt.
Abbey Travel 665.

The work was edited by J.S. Bell, author of Journal of a
Residence in Circassia in the Years 1836 to 1839,
published also by Longman, Brown. Plates include
Mexican mosaics among the ruins of Mitla, the Lake
Aiotlan, the View of Durango from the Sanaurio and
concludes with a group of local Indian costumes.

TORRES-MENDES, Ramon.
Album de Costumbres Columbianas.
Paris, Delarue [c. 1861].

Oblong 4to, 36 handcoloured lithographed plates, original
half red morocco gilt, upper cover gilt direct lettered, raised
band to spine.
Not in Abbey; or Colas.

An apparently scarce set of Columbian costume plates.

VIDAL, Emeric Essex.
Picturesque Illustrations of Buenos Ayres and Monte Video.
London, R. Ackermann, 1820.

First edition. Large 4to, 24 handcoloured aquatints by T.
Sutherland, G. Maile and J. Bluck, after Vidal, four folding, this
copy apparently without watermark,
Colas 3000; Gordon Brown, pg. 123; Martin Hardie, pp. 107,
312; Prideaux pp. 355, 375; Sabin 99460; Tooley (1954), no.
495; Abbey Travel 698; Tooley 495.

The only notable colour plate book in English dealing with
the Argentine (Tooley). Originally issued in monthly parts,
the volume form was then published in two formats with
750 elephant quarto copies and 50 large paper copies. Abbey
and Tooley both state that there were four issued, the first
with parts in wrappers, and three issues in different bindings.
English interest in South America flourished after the capture
of Buenos Aires by Commodore Sir Home Popham and
Colonel Beresford in 1806, who sent booty back to London
with a reported value of £1,200,000. Ackermann exploited

the widespread and substantial interest in South American
affairs that these events had aroused, through a number of
fine publications including these views. There were a number
of quintas in every direction for two or three miles around
the city of Buenos Aires, where embowered among orange,
lemon and fig trees, and covered with vines, they afforded
delicious retirement from the summer heat, excessive in the
arid plains beyond. Those on the banks of La Plata are the
most agreeable. Vidal was paymaster in the British navy and
was one of the most important travelling artists working in
pre- and post-independence South America.

MONTE VIDEO,
From the Anchorage outside the Harbour.

T.Sutherland sculp.

BUENOS AYRES,
From the Bank between the Outer and Inner Roads.

Published May 1 1820 at R.Ackermanns 101 Strand.

32

WALLIS, J., Publisher.
The Costume or the Inhabitants of Peru.
London, Wallis, 1816.

Small 4to, 19 handcoloured aquatint plates, original lithographed boards, title within border, preserved in modern cloth box, spine gilt labelled.
Not in Abbey or Colas; not recorded at auction.

33

WILLYAMS, Rev. Cooper.
An Account of the Campaign in the West Indies in the Year 1794, under the command of their Excellencies Lieutenant General Sir Charles Grey, K.B. and Vice Admiral Sir John Jervis, K.B. Commanders in Chief in the West Indies; with the Reduction of the Islands of Martinique, St. Lucia, Guadaloupe, Marigalante, Desiada, &c. and the events that followed those unparalleled successes, and caused the loss of Guadaloupe.
London, T. Bensley, for G. Nicol...; B. and J. White...; and J. Robson, 1796.

First edition. Folio, preliminaries, dedication, subscription list, iv, 62pp. appendix, 149pp., text, explanation of plates 1 leaf, 6 handcoloured aquatint plates, two engraved maps, one of the Island of Martinique, and a plan of Fort Bourbon now Fort George, and two uncoloured aquatints in text signed C. Willyams del., S. Alken fecit of the entrance to the Harbour of Point a Pitre, and Fleur d'Epee, on large paper, contemporary green morocco gilt ruled, elaborate corner pieces, flat spine, elaborately gilt to military device of armour and flags repeated in compartments, inner gilt dentelle, g.e.
Abbey Travel 677; Cox II, 428; Cundall, West Indies, 2101; Prideaux, 222; Sabin 104563.

All the plates were signed Drawn by the Rev. C. Willyams; S. Alken fecit. Abbey concludes, "The book is beautifully printed and is an excellent example of a 'Bensley' (publisher)." The final plate is of Guadaloupe, the others of Martinique. Copies were sold with the plates in a separate atlas folio or bound.

North America, Canada and Arctica

34

BARTLETT, W.H., artist [and] WILLIS, Nathaniel Parker.
Canada Pittoresque, orne de gravure d'apres les dessins de Bartlett; La Partie Litteraire par Nathaniel Willis… traduit de l'anglais par L. de Baucias.
London, J. Rickerby for George Virtue, 1843.

2 vols. in one, 4to, engraved map, 117 handcoloured steel engraved plates, frontispiece portrait and two engraved title vignettes, later half morocco, spine gilt in compartments, raised bands, t.e.g.
Sabin I, 501; TPK 2424 (for reference); Abbey Travel 651.

Engraved illustrations after W.H. Bartlett, showing landscapes and natural features of the East Coast of America. Sabin states that some proof copies of plates were accompanied with text in French and German as here, signed by Bartlett and Wallis. From Plate 74 all are captioned in the three languages. The map is of the North East part of the United States. Very rare coloured copy printed on special brown paper.

35

BEAUCLERK, Lord Charles.
Lithographic Views of Military Operations in Canada under his Excellency Sir John Colborne, G.C.B., etc. During the Late Insurrection. From Sketches by Lord Charles Beauclerk, Captain Royal Regiment.
London, printed by Samuel Bentley, published by A. Flint, 1840.

Folio, lithographic map, 6 handcoloured lithographic plates after Lord Charles Beauclerk, drawn on stone by N. Hartnell, original printed boards, printed paper labels to spine, plates preserved in modern brown linen covered box.
Allodi Mary "Prints and Early Illustrations" in The Book of Canadian Antiques p. 304; Gagnon II, 124; Loande 1559; Sabin 4164; Spendilove p. 85; TPL 2037.

Rare to find a complete copy of this most comprehensive set of prints dealing with the Papineau Rebellion in Lower Canada (Spendilove). The artist was the third son of the Duke of St. Albans, posted to Canada on active service and took part in the operations depicted and described here.

36

BEYER, Edward.
Album of Virginia. Richmond (Virginia).
Rau & Son of Dresden and W. Loeillot of Berlin, 1858.

Large oblong folio, 40 tinted lithographed plates, plus lithographed title, slightly later half morocco over blindstamped cloth, gilt lettered direct within gilt ruled border, enclosing leaves gilt and coloured, preserved in cloth covered box.
Bennett 10; Howes B413; Sabin 5125.

Attractive album of Virginian mineral springs and other resorts, drawn by Beyer, a graduate of the Dusseldorf Academy of Arts, during a three-year tour of the Old Dominion.

37
BIRCH, William [and] BIRCH, Thomas.
The City of Philadelphia, in the State of Pennsylvania North America: as it appeared in the Year 1800 consisting of Twenty-Eight Plates drawn and engraved by W. Birch & Son. Nr. Neshaminy Bridge on the Bristol Road, Springfield Co., 31 December 1800.

Oblong folio, engraved title by William Barker, vignetted arms of Philadelphia, 30 handcoloured plates copper engraved/etched and published by Campbell, including frontispiece, engraved map, some dated pre-1800, final plate mounted, 19th century half calf over marbled boards, spine gilt lettered, preserved in modern cloth box.
Bennett, p. 13; Deak, Picturing America 228; McGrath p.7.

Birch was a painter and engraver, born in England. He had exhibited some of his views of Philadelphia at the R.A. His miniatures on enamel, of which he made about 60 in America, gave him his chief reputation. He also had a reputation for design.

BLOUET, A.
Chutes du Niagara, Niagara Falls... Sketched from Nature in March, 1837 by A. Blouet. Drawn on Stone by C. Redmond.
Paris, Delpech, 1838.

Large folio, 6 handcoloured lithographed plates, lithographed title, slightly later half calf over marbled boards, spine raised bands, gilt ruled, label.
Adamson Frederic Church's Niagara, p. 148; Dow II, pp. 891-892; Eland 137; Lane, Impressions of Niagara, p. 51; McKinsey 73.

A remarkable set of views of these dramatic waterfalls, catching completely their grandeur.

BROWNE, Lieut. William Henry.
Ten Coloured Views taken during the Arctic Expedition
of H.M.S. "Enterprise" and H.M.S. "Investigator"…
London, Ackermann and Co., 1850.

Folio, 10 tinted lithographed views on 7 plates, two plates
touched by hand in red, original blue cloth panelled in blind.
Arctic Bibliography 2344; Sabin 73366; Abbey Travel 637;
Chavanne, 1450 and 4798; Staton & Tremaine 3047.

Plates signed Lithoed by Chas Haghe, after the original by
Lieut. W.H. Browne and Printed by Day & Son. Dedicated to
the Lords Commissioners of the Admiralty. Where there are
two illustrations on one leaf, each carries the full
signatures. Charles Haghe was Louis Haghe's younger
brother. In 1852 Louis Haghe, who had worked in
company with Day, as Day & Haghe, gave up lithography to
concentrate on water colour painting in 1852. His
younger brother Charles, who had constantly helped him
in his lithography continued in the work.

CATLIN, George.
Catlin's North American Indian Portfolio. Hunting Scenes and Amusements of the Rocky Mountains and Prairies of America. From Drawings and Notes of the Author, made during Eight Years' Travel amongst Forty-Eight of the Wildest and Most Remote Tribes of Savages in North America.
London, George Catlin, Egyptian Hall, Piccadilly, text printed by C. and J. Adlard, 1844.

First edition. Large folio, 25 handcoloured lithographed plates by Catlin after Catlin and McGahey, lithographed by Day and Haghe, each heightened with gum Arabic, letterpress title-page and nine leaves of text, with 20 pp. text and plates coloured with printed captions, later black half morocco over original cloth, upper cover gilt lettered direct.
Sabin 11532; Howes C243; Abbey Travel 653; Field 258; Wagner-Camp-Becker 105a:1; William S. Reese, "The Production of Catlin's North American Indian Portfolio, 1844-1876", unpublished paper.

Catlin himself published the very scarce first coloured issue with the plates printed on full sheets of paper, unmounted. Although Catlin planned on producing a series of thematic portfolios reproducing images from his Indian Gallery, the publication overextended his resources and Henry Bohn took over publication (see following item). Catlin's mother and grandmother had been captured by Indians at the surrender of Forty Fort. His early life was filled with stories, legends and traditions of the "Red Men", not only from his family, but from Revolutionary soldiers, Indian fighters, trappers, hunters and explorers, who were constant guests of the family. Catlin loved fishing and hunting. He qualified as a lawyer and moved to Philadelphia to become a portrait painter in oil and miniature. In 1828 he visited Albany and married Clara B. Gregory who was an enthusiastic aid in his later Western work, accompanying him on many trips. Upon seeing at Philadelphia a delegation of 10 to 15 dignified looking Indians from the wilds of the Far West he resolved "to use my art and so much of the labours of my future life as might be required in rescuing from oblivion the looks and customs of the vanishing races of native man in America". To this end he spent his summers among the Indians and in winter returned to his own life and painted portraits so as to be able to return to his beloved Indians the next year (DAB).

CATLIN, George.
Illustrations of the Manners, Customs, and Conditions of the North American Indians with Letters and Notes…
London, Henry G. Bohn, 1866.

Tenth edition. 8vo, handcoloured frontispiece and 308 handcoloured plates on 176 leaves, 3 handcoloured maps, one folding, slightly later half red morocco, raised bands, appropriate devices on spine in gilt.
Field 260; Howes C241; McCracken 8K; Sabin 11537; Streeter Sale 4277; Wagner-Camp 84.

It is a mark of the popularity of this work that it went into 10 editions in just under 30 years, and that Bohn, who was renowned for the best eye for a publishing winner, which he could publish at a profit but at a more popular price, picked the work up. He had few failures.

CHORIS, Louis.

Voyage Pittoresque autour du Monde [bound with] Vues et Paysages des Regions Equinoxales.
Paris, De l'Imprimerie de Firmin Didot; Chez Paul Renouard, 1826.

Folio, 2p. l., vi, [149], [3]p., frontispiece portrait, 126 handcoloured lithographed plates, folding map, 2 plans, some musical arrangements, title vignette, [second work, 24 handcoloured lithographed views], contemporary quarter calf with marbled sides.
Sabin 12885; Hill 290.

The voyage was from Cronstadt to Chili, then on by the Easter Islands to Kamtchatka, the Gulf of Kotzebue to San Francisco, the Sandwich Islands, via the Aleutians to the Philippines with a notice on the Coral Islands par M. Adelbert de Chamisso. Choris, often known as Louis. One purpose of the voyage was to search for the Northeast Passage. After visiting islands in the South Seas, Kotzebue explored the North American coast and landed twice on the Hawaiian Islands. Choris's work is highly prized for both its beauty and as an historical record. Also included are observations on natural; history by Cuvier and Chamisso and a study of human skulls by Dr. Gall. Complete copies with all the plates coloured are very rare. The book was also issued partially coloured and entirely uncoloured, (see elsewhere in this catalogue for the account of Otto von Kotzebue. Choris an artist of German-Russian parentage born in Kharkov accompanied the Kotzebue expedition as artist on their first circumnavigation. It was the first time that the natives of Kotzebue island had ever seen Europeans and their greetings involved rubbing noses and offering a meal of whale meat) (Hill). See Russian section.

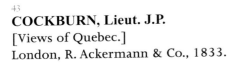

COCKBURN, Lieut. J.P.
[Views of Quebec.]
London, R. Ackermann & Co., 1833.

Oblong folio, 6 finely handcoloured aquatint plates, watermarked J. Whatman, without title or text, apparently as issued, loose in folder, preserved in red morocco backed linen folder, upper cover gilt lettered.
Not in Abbey or Tooley (1954).

Unusual views of Quebec finely executed including Cape Diamond and Wolf's Cove; the Ice Pont formed between Quebec & Point Levi; View of Quebec from below Aubigny Church; the Falls of Montmorency, Quebec in the distance; the Cone of Montmorency and the Lower City of Quebec.

CRESSWELL, Lieut. Samuel Gurney.
A Series of Eight Sketches in Color… of the Voyage of the H.M.S. Investigator during the Discovery of the Northwest Passage.
London, Day and Son, Ackermann and Co., 1854.

Folio, title, description of the plates pp. (1)-4, coloured map of the North West Passage, 8 chromolithographed plates, contemporary three quarter cloth, marbled paper sides.
Abbey Travel 644; Lande 1128; Sabin 17490; TPL 33353.

Plates show the first discovery of land by H.M.S. Investigator, September 1850, the Headland of Baring Island, H.M.S. Investigator penetrating narrow passage between pack ice, Melville Island from Banks' Land. Plates were lithographed by W. Simpson. The author was a Lieutenant on this voyage, which was captained by M'Clure.

DAVIS, Major Henry S.
Views of the Falls of Niagara, Painted on the Spot in the Autumn of 1846. London, Thomas M'Lean, 1848.

Large folio, 4 chromolithographed plates, tinted lithographed headpiece, full page plan of the Niagara River, unbound as issued in original grey paper wrappers, the upper cover with title printed in red and black, modern cloth box with leather label on upper cover.
Not in Abbey or other major colour plate bibliographies.

A very rare view of the Niagara Falls. No copies of this work appear to have come up at auction.

44

DAWSON, Henry B.
Battles of the United States by Sea and Land embracing those of the Revolution and Indian Wars; the War of 1812, and the Mexican War.
New York, Johnson, Fry & Co., [1858].

2 vols., 4to, 39 coloured plates, original cloth.
Sabin 18931; Larned 2524.

A comprehensive look at the Indian Wars as well as the Mexican Wars, attractively illustrated.

DUFLOS, Pierre Le Jeune.
Recueil d'Estampes representant les Grades, les Rangs & les Dignetes, suivant le Costume de toutes les Nations existantes.
Chez Duflos, le jeune, 1779-[1784].

Folio, original parts, 235 (of 264) handcoloured engraved plates, wrappers, labels laid down on front covers, uncut.
Colas 2508; Lipperheide 38; Brunet II, 862; Cohen de Ricci 334; Rahir 407; Vinet 2104.

This collection of costume plates originally appeared in 44 parts each with 6 engraved handcoloured plates. They were engraved by Pierre Duflos, Mme Duflos or Marillier after drawings by Jean Touze. The plates were divided up into Continents and showed the Rulers, the leaders of every religion, the Magistrature, the Men of Letters and the Artists. Included here are native rulers of America in their traditional dress (Louisiana).

FISCHER, Alvan.
[Views of LaGrange. The Residence of General Lafayette. Boston, by Le Villain in Paris for A. Fischer, 1826.]

Folio, 4 handcoloured lithographed plates, unbound as issued in original green paper wrappers, letterpress title printed on upper cover, preserved in black cloth chemise and slipcase.

Scarce and finely worked plates of the residence of General Lafayette.

48

49

49

FRANKLIN, Captain Sir John.
Narrative of a Journey to the Shores of the Polar Sea, in the Years 1819, 20, 21 and 22.
London, John Murray, 1823.

4to, 31 plates, 9 handcoloured aquatint plates, two coloured line-engravings, others uncoloured line engravings, four engraved folding maps, contemporary half calf gilt.
Abbey Travel 635; Chavanne No. 4268; Sabin 25624; Staton & 'Tremaine 1248, 1434; Graff 1406; Peel 80; Arctic Bibliography 5194; Wagner-Camp 23:1.
Bound with:
FRANKLIN, Captain Sir John. Narrative of a Second Expedition to the Shores of the Polar Sea, in the Years 1825, 1826, and 1827...
London, John Murray, 1828.
4to, 30 plates, 2 handcoloured line engravings, six folding engraved maps, contemporary half calf gilt.
Abbey Travel 635; Chavanne No. 4269; Sabin 25628; Field 561; Graff 1407; Peel 88; Arctic Bibliography 5198.

Each volume was published separately at £4.4s. in boards. The volumes were advertised together after 1828 in "boards" but in the early days of cloth bindings a binding in cloth boards was not always so specified. Two of the maps are the same in both the above volumes, and one of these, in Vol. I, Map no. 3, has the imprint altered to the later date, 1828, a further indication, besides the binding, that these volumes were issued at the same time, despite the title-page dates. Franklin was knighted in 1829 (Abbey).

HERIOT, George.
Travels through the Canadas containing a Description of
the Picturesque Scenery on Some of the Rivers and
Lakes. With an Account of the Production, Commerce,
and Inhabitants of those Provinces.
London, Richard Phillips, 1807.

Folio, 26 handcoloured aquatint plates (of 27), contemporary
half morocco, spine gilt in compartments, raised bands, m.e.
Gagnon Vol. I; Prideaux, pp. 229, 255, 340; Sabin 31489;
Staton & Tremaine 805; Abbey 618 (for mention).

Abbey lists map of the River St. Lawrence to accompany the
plates. Each illustration has separate title, signatures and
imprint. Plates include views of Quebec, Canadian dances,
encampment of Domiciliated Indians and their costume;
the falls of Montmorenci, of Chaudiere, of La Puce with its
lower fall, the city of Montreal, and the Niagara Falls. Plate
No. 6 is a line engraving, the remainder are coloured
aquatints, some slightly heightened with gum Arabic. It
would seem that the plates were not originally available
separately. Plates imprinted G. Heriot Esqr pinxt and most
were engraved by F.C. Lewis, J.C. Stadler, Cartwright.

51

HICKMAN, William.

Sketches on the Nipisaguit, a River in New Brunswick, B.N. America.

Halifax, N.S., John B. Strong, London, Day & Son, Lithographers, 1860.

Small folio, preliminaries, introductory chapter, 1 leaf, text 8 leaves unnumbered, imprint of Day & Son at foot of recto of last leaf, publisher's cloth stamped in gilt and blind, 8 tinted lithographed plates in two tints, coloured, original blindstamped and gilt decorated cloth, spine flat and gilt ruled. Abbey Travel 629; Staton & Tremaine 3988; Sabin cites 31706 for 1861 edition; not in Lande.

That Day thought it worth inserting the ticket, noted under Binding, is probably a sign of the extent to which, despite the comparative transport difficulties of those days, American or Canadian sheets and plates were imported into the country, as is seen elsewhere in this collection. It would obviously be exceptional for it to be worth re-manufacturing a Canadian book in Britain, and that a work on the Nipisaguit should receive this treatment is perhaps surprising (Abbey).

51

52

HODGES, James.
Construction of the Great Victoria Bridge in Canada by
James Hodges Engineer to Messrs. Peto, Brassey, and Betts
Contractors.
London, John Weale, Kell Bros Lithrs… Designed by John
Thomas, 1860.

Folio, preliminaries, 104pp., text, 26 lithographed plates, two
chromolithographed, 6 in two tints, 3 one tint, 20 in one tint
and printed in gold and one colour, another tinted in one tint;
the remainder plans in lithographed line, including
lithographed title, 42 plans, publisher's full red morocco, gilt
borders and spine gilt in compartments, centre panel with gilt
medallion, blindstamped panelling to centre of sides, morocco
labels gilt, g.e.
Abbey Travel 631 (for the ordinary edition; Sabin 32342);
Staton & Tremaine No. 3914; Spendlove, The Face of Early
Canada, pp. 73-76.

The British Museum copy is evidently from a special
edition in one folio volume in which each page and plate
other than the diagrams is bordered in gilt. The work ends
with a plan for a proposed tubular bridge, for crossing the
Niagara Gorge. The title verso is with imprint Bradbury
and Evans. The Victoria Bridge was a railway bridge and
shows passenger and mail crossing the river, by C.
Krieghoff, who also famously drew Indian Chiefs. There is
also a plate of the Grand Trunk Railway of Canada, Victoria
Bridge, over the River St. Lawrence at Montreal. Plates after
John Duncan, W.O. Gooding; J.W. Woodford, J. Duncan.
H.H. Killaly. Sabin describes this work as "a most
important and valuable engineering work". The work was
dedicated to Albert, Prince of Wales "who graciously
visited Canada, to inaugurate the opening of the Victoria
Bridge… across the St. Lawrence".

Abbildung der Bewohner des Kotzebue Sundes.

54

53

JANSON, Charles William.

The Stranger in America containing Observations made during a long Residence in that Country, on the Genius, Manners and Customs of the People of the U.S., with biographical Particulars; Hints and Facts relative to the Arts, Sciences, Commerce, Agriculture, Manufactures, Emigration, and the Slave Trade.
London, Albion Press, Printed for James Cundee, 1807.

4to, engraved title, half title, preface pages (v) to xiii; errata, page (xiv); contents, pp. (15) to 22; text pp. 1-49 [9]; directions to binder, p. (500); advertisements for James Cundee, 6pp., Plan of the City of Philadelphia, 10 handcoloured aquatint plates, tinted aquatint illustration at foot of pg. 197.
Abbey Travel 649.

A second edition was published by Tegg in 1815. Plates include Boston, Philadelphia, Long Island.

54

KOTZEBUE, Otto von.

Entdeckungs-Reise in die Sud-See und nach der Berings Strasse zur Erforschung einer nordostlichen Durchfahrt. Unternommenin den Jahren 1815, 1816, 1817, and 1818. Weimar, Gebrudern Hoffman, 1821.

First edition. 3 vols., 4to, Vol. I, frontispiece and double page plate; Vol. II frontispiece and 4 plates (3 double page), map; Vol. III, frontispiece, 12 plates, two folding tables, 5 folding maps, all engraved aquatints, handcoloured, contemporary quarter calf over boards.
Howes K258; Sabin 38264; Hill 943.

The Rurik rounded the Cape Horn and visited Chile, Easter Island and the Marshall Islands. Kotzebue explored the North American coast and Hawaii and searched unsuccessfully for a passage to the Arctic Ocean. The description of the northwest coast of America is a most important contribution. The second volume contains a description of California.

This was the second Russian expedition into the Pacific for scientific exploration, sponsored by Count Romanzoff, and commanded by Lieutenant Kotzebue, and also included the artist Ludovik Choris (see earlier entry).

LEWIS, James Otto.
[The Aboriginal Portfolio; or a Collection of Portraits of the most Celebrated Chiefs of the North American Indians.] [Philadelphia, printed by Lehman & Duval, published by the author, 1836-38, i.e. May 1835-February 1836.]

Folio, red half morocco and black cloth boards; original blue printed wrappers to Part No. 5 bound in. Three letterpress broadside prospectuses "advertisement" leaves to parts 1-3 bound before plates 1, 9, & 17, in total 72 handcoloured lithographed plates (of 80) after Lewis by Lehman & Duval, colour photographs of Plates 73 through 80.
Bennett, p. 68; Eberstadt 131:418; Field 936; Howes L315; Reese National Character...23; Sabin 40812.

This work which is scarcer than McKenney and Hall, Maximilian's Reise or Catlin's North American Indian Portfolio, records the dress of the Potawatomi, Winnebago, Shawnee, Sioux, Miami, Fox, Iowa and other tribes at treaties of Prairie du Chien, Fort Wayne, Fond du Lac and Green Bay. Publication of the work was costly and time consuming. The work was originally issued in 10 parts with 8 plates per number in printed wrappers. The publisher was forced into bankruptcy while part 9 was in the press, however, reducing the edition and forcing part 10 to be just barely finished and sparsely distributed. A projected 11th part would have contained "Historical and Biographical Description of the Indians," but was never completed. The front wrappers bear a lithographic portrait vignette and the note "Subscription price $2.0 per Number issued Monthly until 10 numbers are Complete". Only one copy has been known to have had the lithographed title, that of the Jay T. Snider Collection of Historical Americana.

Lehman & Duval Lith.rs

THE SUN

A Miami Chief

Painted at the treaty of Mississinewa 1827 by J.O. Lewis.

56
MARRYAT, Frank [Francis S.].
Mountains, Molehills or Recollections of a Burnt Journal.
London, Longman Brown, Green and Longmans, 1855.

8vo, 8 chromolithographed plates, red morocco backed boards.
Howes M299.

Americans were not the only people who travelled to California seeking fortune and fame. This is the story of the recollections of a well-to-do but slightly eccentric British adventurer who travelled to the Americas in 1850, hoping to find and record whatever his British audience would find exotic or interesting. Readers will find accounts in this work of horse races, animal hunts, bear and bull fights, and other oddities of Californian society which may help illuminate the larger culture in which their ancestors lived. Marryat returned to England in 1853 to write of his experiences. He was the son of Frederick Marryat who wrote Mr Midshipman Easy and other books, and himself wrote a travel account of Borneo and the Indian Archipelago.

57
MAY, Commander Walter William, R.N.
A Series of Fourteen Sketches made during the Voyage up Wellington Channel in Search of Sir John Franklin, K.C.H. and the missing crews of H.M. Discovery-ships Erebus and Terror: together with a short account of each drawing.
London, Day & Son, May 1, 1855.

4to, title, description of plates pp. 2-6; list of subscribers, 1 leaf, 14 coloured lithographed plates on 13 sheets, signed Commr W.W. May R.N. del, Day & Son Lithrs to the Queen, modern half burgundy morocco over marbled boards, spine raised bands, gilt in compartments.
Sabin 47083 (dated 1865); Abbey Travel 646; Staton & Tremaine 3454.

Plates after Commander May and lithographed by J. Needham, T.G. Dutton, some with no lithographer given. The Erebus and Terror had been involved in an Antarctic Expedition 1839-43 under the command of James Clark Ross to measure the earth's magnetic field in the Southern Hemisphere and to locate the South magnetic pole and there are oil paintings by J.W. Carmichael at the National Maritime of these two ships on service in New Zealand.

McKENNEY, Thomas Loraine [and] HALL, James.
History of the Indian Tribes of North America, with Biographical Sketches and Anecdotes of the Principal Chiefs...
Philadelphia, T.K. & P.G. Collins for Edward C. Biddle (Vol. I), Frederick W. Greenough (Vol. II), and Daniel Rice & James G. Clark (Vol. III), [1834-] 1836-42-44.

First edition, first issue. 3 vols., large folio, errata slip, 120 handcoloured lithographed plates after Charles Bud King, James Orno Lewis, P. Rhindsbacher and R.M. Sully, uncoloured lithographed map, contemporary half morocco.
BAL 6934; Bennett, p. 79; Field 992; Howes M129; Lipperheide Mc4; Reese American Color Plate Books 24; Sabin 43410OA

"The grandest colour plate book issued in the United States up to the time of its publication" – Reese. Its long and checkered publication history spanned twelve years and involved multiple lithographers (the foremost Peter S. Duval and James T. Bowen) and publishers, but the final product is one of the most distinctive and important books in Americana. Almost all the plates are portraits of individual native Americans, the majority painted from life by Charles Bird King (who also reworked the less skilful portraits of James Otto Lewis; see elsewhere). The complicated circumstances of its production have left a large number of bibliographical problems of issues and issue points which have not yet been satisfactorily resolved.

The practice of painting portraits of the principal American Indians who came to Washington had begun as early as 1824. Chiefly painted by King, they were deposited in the War Department. Colonel McKenney, Superintendent of Indian Affairs in Washington, conceived of the plan of making a collection of biographies, enhanced by the addition of the portraits. A biographical sketch accompanies each portrait and the work also contains a general history of the various Indian tribes within the borders of the United States of America.

M'CLURE, Captain Robert Le Mesurier and OSBORNE, Sherard.
The Discovery of the North-West Passage by H.M.S. Investigator.
London, Longman, Brown, Green, Longmans, & Roberts, 1856.

8vo, coloured folding map of the North West Passage, 4 handcoloured lithographed plates signed L.G. Cresswell del. and Hullmandel & Walton lith., plates on card, 19th century half buckram over marbled boards, spine gilt lettered, original upper wrapper bound in.
Chavanne 1538; Sabin 43073; Staton & Tremaine 3451 (the 1865 edition).

Captain M'Clure in H.M.S. Investigator, who had sailed through the Baring Strait, was forced to abandon ship in the Bay of Mercy, Melville Islaned, where he had been frozen in. The rescue was set in hand by Captin Kellett with the Resolute and the Intrepid, approaching from the Atlantic. The Investigators joined these ships after a sledge journey, so that the North West passage was completed on foot.

WA - PEL - LA

CHIEF OF THE MUSQUAKEES.

PUBLISHED BY F. W. GREENOUGH, PHILAD.ª

Drawn Printed & Coloured at I.T.Bowen's Lithographic Establishment Nº 94. Walnut St

Entered according to act of Congress in the Year 1838 by F.W.Greenough in the Clerks Office of the District Court of the Eastern District of Penn.ª

CRIMSON CLIFFS.
A View of the Coloured Snow in Lat. 76. 25 N. & Long. 65. W.

60

60

ROSS, John.
A Voyage of Discovery, made under orders of the Admirality, in His Majesty's Ships Isabella and Alexander, for the purpose of exploring Baffin's Bay, and inquiring into the probability of a North-West Passage…
London, John Murray, 1819.

First edition. 4to, 25 plates, some folding, 15 handcoloured, aquatints, 6 uncoloured aquatints, one uncoloured line and stipple engraving and one uncoloured line engraving, and seven charts, all but one folding, contemporary polished calf, gilt fillets, spine gilt in compartments, raised bands, m.e.
Abbey Travel 634; Hill, p. 261; Sabin 73376; Staton & Tremaine 1152; Prideaux 255. 350; Chavanne 4909.

61

ROSS, John.
Narrative of a Second Voyage in Search of a North-West Passage, and of a Residence in the Arctic Regions during the Years 1829-1833… and the Discovery of the Northern Magnetic Pole.
London, A.W. Webster, 1835.

First edition. 2 vols., 4to, 45 plates, (20 of these in Appendix), 21 coloured, six lithographed, other uncoloured steel engravings, and 3 mezzotints, two plates expressly signed printed in colours, probably black and blue with red added by hand, five charts, folding map Together with: Appendix, 1835 in second vol., original cloth over boards, spine gilt lettered within decorative border.
Abbey Travel 636; Sabin 73381; Staton & Tremaine 1898; Burch pg. 95.

63

62

ROUS, The Hon. Henry John, Admiral [and] SCHETKEY, John Christian, artist.
A Series of four Sketches, illustrative of various Situations of His Majesty's Ship Pique.
Printed by Trives & Maynard, Portsea, [1835].

Oblong folio, I leaf text, 4 handcoloured lithographed plates, original buff printed wrappers, on upper cover inscription Presented to Admiral Sir John Napier. Only 10 copies handcoloured; a rare naval item.
Abbey Life 343.

Mr Schetkey presumes that the following minutes of the Court Martial, together with Captain the Hon. H.J. Rous's Letter to the Lords Commissioners of the Admiralty, and their Lordships' Letter to him previous to the paying off of His Majesty's Ship Pique, will be a sufficient explanation of these Sketches.

Plates are of the forging over the reef off Cape Forteau; At the moment of carrying away her Rudder; In tow of the French Brig Suffren; As she appear's in Dock at Portsmouth. Schetkey was a celebrated marine painter.

63

RUSSELL, W.H.
The Atlantic Telegraph.
London, Day & Son, [1865].

4to, 26 chromolithographed plates, one a lithographed chart, by Robert Dudley, original cloth with arms of the Royal Cruising Club, surrounded by marine devices gilt on coloured onlays, together with flags of the U.S.A. and Great Britain.
Wheeler Gift 1622.

Russell was the famous war correspondent who made his reputation with his dispatches in the Crimea.

64

SHORT, Richard.
Six Perspective Views on Belle-Isle.
London [published by Richard Short], May-October, 1763.

Oblong folio, 6 handcoloured plates, engraved by Canot and Mason, unbound as issued, new olive wrappers, blue morocco box with morocco label on upper cover.
Sabin 80569.

Belle-Isle was a small rugged island at the entrance to the Straits of Belle-Isle, which gave access into the St. Lawrence waterway. Described in 1911 it was said that several lighthouses had been built on the island. This waterway was open only a few months a year, being blocked with ice at other times. A scarce and beautiful set of plates. Short, who was present at the siege of Quebec, also wrote a book on Nova Scotia.

65

65

SKETCHES IN NEW BRUNSWICK,

taken principally with the intention of shewing the Nature and Description of the Land in the Tract Purchased by the New Brunswick and Nova Scotia Land Company in the Year 1833; and of illustrating the operations of the Association during the Years 1834, & 1835. London, Ackermann & Co., printed by Day & Haghe, 1836.

Folio, lithographed title signed by artist, 12 handcoloured lithographed plates, by W.P. Kay, E.N. Kendal, P. Harry, lithographed by S. Russell and Day & Haghe, slightly later morocco backed pebbled cloth, original stiff grey wrapper bound in; preserved in blue buckram slipcase and box, black morocco lettering piece on spine.
TPL 1907; Abbey Travel 623; Lande 2035; Sabin 81551; Spendlove p. 35. Staton ;& Tremaine 1907.

No public price has been found and it is likely that the work was produced for private circulation. The plates show the encampment of the surveying party at the site of Stanley; and include the mill dam at Stanley and its erection; general scenes in and around Stanley and Winter View looking up the River St. John.

66

SMYTH, Coke.
Sketches in the Canadas.
London, Tho. M'Lean, [1840].

Large folio, lithographed title with handcoloured vignette,
lithographed dedication, verso list of drawings, and 22 plates
handcoloured lithographs, all mounted on card and loose,
preserved in brown morocco backed linen covered box, spine
gilt banded and gilt lettered direct.
Abbey Travel 625; Lande 2215; Sabin 85203; Gagnon I,
3341; Staton & Tremaine 2549; Tooley (1954) 460.

Fine plates include views of Quebec, the Niagara Falls;
Zity a Huron Indian; the Montmorency Falls; Buffalo
Hunting; Rapids of St. Lawrence; Niagara River.

Published in 1840 at £6.6s plain or at £8.8s. coloured
and mounted, according to the Publisher's Circular.
Unless the colouring in the above copy is not original the
book must also have been issued with the plates coloured,
but unmounted. Sabin, who says that the mounted copies
were in a portfolio, without the lithographed leaf of text,
suggests that they were a later issue. The Publisher's
Circular advertisement, however, suggests that this was
not the case.

66

POSTING ON THE ST. LAWRENCE

67

WARRE, Henry James.
Sketches in North America and the Oregon Territory.
[London], Dickenson & Co., [c. 1848].

Folio, 16 handcoloured lithographed plates, letterpress title, dedication, one map, 20 views, plates on card with single gilt line surrounding each, contemporary half red morocco gilt, gilt lettered on upper cover, spine gilt, raised bands.
Graff 4543; Howes W1114; Sabin 100455; Wagner-Camp 157.

"The plates issued in two forms, black and white and tinted. It is possible some were issued coloured by hand, but more likely that copies were coloured by the purchaser. Seems from correspondence, that the officers were sent by the British Government with the intention of fortifying the mouth of the Columbian river.

(69)

Africa, Atlantic and Canary Islands

68

ALBERTI, Lodwyk.
Description Physique et Historique des Caffres sur la Cote Meridionale de l'Afrique.
Amsterdam, E. Maaskamp, 1811.

8vo, 1p. text, 2 handcoloured lithographed plates, folding plan, 4 folio handcoloured lithographed plates by De Cher Howen; J. Smies; L. Portman, in later marbled wrappers, preserved in folio box, green morocco over tan cloth.
Mendelssohn/Kennedy; Landwehr 218.

Alberti accompanied General J.W. Janssens when he travelled to the Cape as Governor of the Colony under the Batavian Republic in 1802. Alberti was a Captain in the Fifth Battalion of the Corps de Waldeck, and the next year was sent to Fort Frederick in Algoa Bay, where he took direction of affairs relating to the Kaffirs and Hottentots, and acted as landrost. The original drawings were done on the spot by Baron de Howen and worked up by Smies in Amsterdam and then engraved and aquatinted by Portman. Howen was a Russian officer of artillery, obviously a gifted amateur and Jacob Smies, known chiefly as a caricaturist was employed to give the work professional polish.

69

ALLEN Commander William.
Fernando Po from Nature and on Stone. N.p., 1838.

Oblong 4to, 4 handcoloured aquatint plates plus two folding plates, these captioned in pencil, in original publisher's buff wrappers, preserved in cloth covered slipcase.
Abbey Travel 283.

Fernando Po was a Spanish island off the coast of West Africa, in the Bight of Benin, named after a 16th century Portuguese explorer. A volcanic outcrop, the island had rich vegetation, dense undergrowth and crops including sugar cane, cotton and indigo plants. Tropical wildlife included crocodiles and turtles. The mountains reached a height of 4000/6000 ft. and contained craters. The dry season was from November to January. The population of 25,000 was mostly Spaniards. The principal settlement was Saint Clarence, used by the British as a naval station for ships engaged in suppressing the slave trade.

ALLEN, Commander William.

Picturesque Views on the River Niger, Sketched during Lander's last Visit in 1832-1833.

London, W. Clowes & Sons for John Murray, Hodgson & Graves and Ackermann, 1840.

Oblong 4to, 2pp. subscribers list at rear, dedication to Prince Albert, lithographed map, 22 tinted lithographed views on 10 plates, one folding panorama, all after Allen and drawn on stone by Allen, W.L. Walton, T. Picken and C. Haghe, all printed by Day & Haghe, original printed wrappers, preserved in modern linen covered folder, label on spine.
Abbey Travel 284.

Allen took part in the Niger expedition of Richard Lander and Oldfield, 1832; but is best known as having commanded the Wilberforce in the elaborately equipped but disastrous expedition under Captain Trotter to the same river in 1841-2. In 1849 he published a "Plan for the immediate Extinction of the Slave Trade, for the Relief of the West India Colonies, and for the diffusion of Civilisation and Christianity in Africa by the co-operation of Mammon with Philanthropy." Allen was a Fellow of the Royal Society and some of his landscape paintings were exhibited at the Royal Academy from 1828-47 (DNB). See also Graves Catalogue.

CLIFFS AT ATTÀH.

T. Picken, lith.

Day & Haghe Lith.rs to the Queen.

MOUNTAINS & MARKET CANOES NEAR BOKWÈH.

T. Picken, lith.

Day & Haghe Lith.rs to the Queen.

London. Published Sept.r 1840. by John Murray.—Hodgson & Graves.—Ackermann & Co.

ANGAS, George French.

The Kaffirs Illustrated in a Series of Drawings taken among the Amazulu, Amapanda, and Amakaza tribes; also portraits of the Hottentot, Malay, Fingo, and other races inhabiting Southern Africa: together with sketches of landscape scenery in the Zulu Country.
London, G. Barclay for J. Hogarth, 1849.

Folio, lithographed portrait frontispiece of the author on India proof paper, engraved subscribers list, 29 (numbered I-XXIX), handcoloured lithographed plates after Angas, drawn on stone by Angas, J. Needham, A. Laby, B.W. Hawkins or W. Wing, printed by Charles Lovell, M.& N. Hanhart, Hullmandel & Walton, woodengraved vignette illustrations, later half morocco over brown cloth, spine gilt lettered direct.
Abbey Travel I, 339; Colas 134; Gay 3157; Mendelssohn I, p. 45; Tooley 60.

An outstanding work, particularly for its portraits of the Zulus. Includes views of Cape Town, Hottentot Holland, Somerset West and Durban.

With a taste for travel and draughtsmanship, Angas perfected his art in 1842, studying anatomical drawing in London and also learned the art of lithography. He spent two years in South Africa and published the result of his work in 1849 in this imperial folio work. Much of his other work was undertaken in South Australia and New Zealand, see elsewhere in this catalogue.

BAINES, Thomas.
The Victoria Falls Zambesi River sketched on the spot
(during the journey of J. Chapman & T. Baines).
London, Day & Son, Limited, 1865.

First edition. Large folio, tinted lithographic title with large
coloured vignette view, 10 tinted lithographed plates all coloured
by hand, drawn on stone by T. Picken, R.M. Bryson, F. Jones and
E. Walker, all after Baines and printed by Day & Son, original
blue blindstamped cloth, gilt lettered direct on upper cover.
The Chatsworth copy. Kennedy B58-68.

Handcoloured issue of Baine's most important published
work. Baines arrived in the Cape Colony in 1842 and from
1848-1851 he accompanied the British army in the Kafir
war as artist and in 1855 joined an expedition which was
appointed under Mr A. Gregory to explore North-West
Australia. His energy and skill during his appointment
secured for him the special thanks of the colonial
government, and in 1858, at the recommendation of the
Royal Geographical Society, he was appointed artist to the
Zambesi expedition under Livingstone, whom he
accompanied as far as Tete in the Portuguese territory. In
1861 he joined Chapman in his expedition from the
south-west coast to the Victoria Falls, where as well as
making a complete route survey, as well as naturalist and
scientific notes, he made a number of sketches and
paintings, his drawings of the Victoria Falls, reproduced in
large coloured lithographs, formed this spectacular folio.

73

BARNIM, Adalbert Freiherr [and] Robert Hartmann.
Reise in Nordest Afrika.
Berlin, Verlag G. Reimer, [1863].

First edition. 8vo text vol. to accompany plates. Oblong folio, elaborate pictorial title printed in colours and gold, double page lithographed view of Alexandria, 23 single page tinted lithographed plates, 9 printed in colour, by Bellerman, original green cloth gilt lettered direct to upper cover. Hilmy I, 290.

The author recorded tribal and animal life, with particular attention to the giraffes, hippopotami, lions etc. He also depicted views of cities and monuments.

BARROW, Sir John.
An Account of Travels into the Interior of Southern
Africa, in which are described the Character and the
Condition of the Dutch Colonists of the Cape of Good
Hope, and of several Tribes of Natives beyond its Limits,
the Natural History... and the Geography of the
Southern Extremity of Africa.
London, Strahan & Preston, for T. Cadell & W. Davies,
1806.

Second edition. 2 vols., 4to, 8 handcoloured aquatints by T.
Medland after Samuel Daniell, 9 engraved charts and maps, 3
folding maps, handcoloured in outline, 6 charts, contemporary
polished calf, thin decorative border, spine flat and gilt in
compartments, raised bands.
Abbey Travel I, 322; Gay 2996; Mendelssohn I, p.88; Tooley 85.

Barrow accompanied an expedition from Cape Town to
Graaff-Reinet, and another to Namaqualand, and he gives
an excellent description of the country traversed,
particularly with regard to the botany and zoology of
those regions.

BELLASIS, George Hutchins.
Views of Saint Helena.
London, John Tyler, 1815.

Oblong folio, 6 numbered handcoloured aquatints by Robert
Havell after Bellasis, printed by W.B. McQueen, text printed on
rectos only, original printed wrappers, preserved in 20th
century morocco backed cloth folder, upper cover gilt lettered.
Abbey Travel I, 309; Tooley 87.

The earliest views of St. Helena recorded in Abbey.
Bellasis made an eight months' residence on the island
shortly before the arrival of Napoleon. The work is
dedicated to the Duke of Wellington who had restored
"the peace and liberties of Europe" and "made the island
an object of interest to the whole world". Plate 3 shows
the Briars, the intended residence of Bonaparte, which
was at the head of the valley.

S. Daniell del. *T. Medland sculp.*

Kaffer Woman

Published Feb.ʳ 14. 1806, by Mess.ʳˢ Cadell & Davies Strand London.

74

BERNATZ, Johan Martin.
Scenes in Ethiopia Designed from Nature... With Descriptions of the Plates and Extracts from a Journal of Travel in that Country. In two Parts. Part I – Lowlands of the Danakil. Part II – The Highlands of Shoa.
London, Bradbury & Evans for F.G. Moon, 1852.

2 parts in one vol., oblong folio, printed title, tinted decorative lithographed titles to Vol. I & II, uncoloured lithographed map, 47 lithographed plates by Leopold Rottman after Bernatz, tinted in five colours (this copy heightened by hand, includes one double page plate painted by Sebastian Minsinger or Julius Adam of Munich.

Not in Abbey; Brunet I, 798 (incorrect plate count), "bel ouvrage"; cf. Colas 310; Gay 2586.

The German-born artist Johann Bernatz accompanied Major Cornwallis Harris as official artist on his mission to open up trading links with the ancient Ethiopian kingdom of Shoa. The present work is probably the most important work to result from that expedition. It includes the first scenes of Shawa ever produced. The plates depict (amongst other subjects) Oromo dancing, a slave caravan, King Sahla Sellase sitting in judgement, an Easter banquet, costume, etc.

78

BOILAT, Abbe P.D.

Esquisses Senegalaises, Physionomie du Pays &
Peuplades – Commerce – Religions – Passe et Avenir –
Recits et Legendes.
Paris, P. Bertrand, 1853.

First edition. 2 vols., 8vo, text vol., half title, large coloured
folding map, 4to atlas vol. with folding coloured map of
Senegal, and [24] coloured lithographed plates by Llanta, and
printed by Lemercier in Paris, 8vo vol, 1pp. title advertisement
leaf, description of plates, text xvi pp., half title, dedication,
preface, 496pp of text, conclusion, index, errata,
Brunet 28421; Gay 2886; Colas 364; Graesse 471.

Colour plate books on West Africa are uncommon.
Probably unique in recording the people and costume of
Senegal. In addition the plates are of very high quality.

BOWDITCH, Thomas Edward.

Excursions in Madeira and Porto Santo, during the
autumn of 1823, while on his third voyage to Africa. To
which is added by Mrs Bowditch, I. A narrative of the
continuance of the voyage to its completion, together
with subsequent occurrences from Bowditch's arrival in
Africa to the Period of his Death. II. A Description of the
English Settlements on the River Gambia. III. Appendix:
containing zoological and botanical descriptions, and
translation from the Arabic.
London, George B. Whittaker, 1825.

First edition. 4to, 22 lithographed plates, of which four are
handcoloured and three folding, woodengravings in text,
contemporary half calf.
Abbey Travel 190; Gay 2983; Colas 418.
Plate 9, Costume of the Gambia, which is coloured, is lacking
in the Abbey copy.

An enjoyable excursion by the author and his wife in
Madeira en route to Ashantee.

BOWDITCH, Thomas Edward.
Mission from Cape Coast Castle to Ashantee, with a Statistical Account of that Kingdom, and Geographical Notices of other Parts of the Interior of Africa.
London, W. Bulmer & Co. for John Murray, 1819.

First edition. 4to, half title, 11 plates and plans including two engraved maps, one folding, woodengraved letterpress plan, folding engraved plate, 7 fine handcoloured aquatint plates by Bowditch, 5pp. engraved sheet music on 3 leaves, uncut in original boards, rebacked in paper, original label laid down.
Abbey Travel 194; Colas 418.

"This work is the most important after Bruce's excited great interest, as an almost incredible story… of a land and people of warlike and barbaric splendour hitherto unknown" (DNB). In 1815 the African Company planned a mission to Ashantee, and appointed Bowditch the conductor. Bowditch was forced to supersede his chief and succeeded in a most difficult negotiation, and formed a treaty with the King of Ashantee, which promised peace on the Gold Coast. He must be considered as the first who achieved the object of penetrating to the interior of Africa.

BOWLER, T.W.
Four Views of Cape Town, Cape of Good Hope, Drawn from Nature…and Lithographed by Day and Haghe.
Cape Town, J.E. Collard, [1844].

Folio, 4 handcoloured lithographed plates, original printed wrappers, preserved in burgundy morocco backed black cloth.
ASIB & Bowler Biography, p. 260.

"Bowler was a landscape painter. He was appointed assistant astronomer under Sir T. Maclear at the Cape. After four years he resigned and established himself as artist and teacher of drawing. It is recorded in the DNB that his lithographs were in the style of Harding and showed facility in handling the chalk and some power of composition.

BOWLER, Thomas William.
South African Sketches a Series of Ten of the most interesting Views at the Cape of Good Hope.
London, Day & Son, Ackermann & Co., and S. Robertson of Capetown, 1854.

Folio, 9 handcoloured lithographs engraved by J. Needham after sketches by Bowler, and lithographed by Day & Son, including title, red cloth backed thin card wrappers, modern tan cloth folder and slipcase with morocco label on spine.

Abbey Travel 343; Gordon Brown, pp. 50, 56-7; Kenney Catalogue of Prints in the South African Museum, Johannesburg, 1975, I B254-263.

He painted a panorama of the district, and published in 1844 Four Views of Cape Town (see above); also this series of ten lithographs of scenes at the Cape of Good Hope in 1865 and (see below) Kafir Wars, a series of 20 views with descriptive letterpress by W.R. Thomson. He exhibited two of his Cape views at the Royal Academy in 1860 (DNB).

BOWLER, Thomas William and THOMSON, W.R.
The Kaffir Wars and the British Settlers in South Africa. A Series of Views from original Sketches…Descriptive Letterpress by W.R. Thomson.
London, Day & Sons, J.C. Juta, Cape Town and Port Elizabeth; Graham's Town, C. Nixdorff, and Edinburgh, 1865.

First edition. Large 4to, handcoloured lithographed frontispiece mounted on card as issued and 19 tinted lithographed plates after the author by E. Jones, original brown pebble grained cloth, lettered in gilt on upper cover, g.e.
Not in Abbey or Tooley; Bradlow & Gordon-Brown pp. 195-198, plates 99-118; Mendelssohn I, 176-77.

By the "David Roberts of South African book illustration." Inspired by friend and fellow writer David Baines, Bowler embarked on the Waldensian in December 1861 for his tour of the Eastern Frontier districts, returning at the end of January 1862 with numerous drawings which formed the basis of this book. The views are reproduced in treble tinted lithography and show localities which achieved fame during the eastern frontier struggles. In his introduction the artist expresses the hope that his work if not found very useful in the library among more exhausting books of travel…will be thought ornamental in the drawing room. The work is considered to be amongst Bowler's finest, particularly the views of Port Elizabeth and its harbour. From a geographical point of view, Bowler's Kafir War series cannot be overestimated. They show the changing face and contours of the Eastern Province and Border districts more forcibly than the most fluent writing. The gentle streams flowing through wild and dense undergrowth, over rocky ledges; the cattle grazing on the abundant greenery in the native villages of Chumie and Burns Hill, are now to be seen only in the albums of Bowler and Baines. Encroaching civilisation has altered the Border districts to such an extent, that it is hard to believe that these pictures were not merely a figment of Bowler's imagination (Bradlow).

83

BOWLER, THOMAS William.
Pictorial Album of Cape Town, with Views of Simon's Town, Port Elizabeth, and Graham's Town.
Cape Town, J.C. Juta, 1866.

Oblong folio, 44pp., 12 handcoloured lithographed plates, after author by M.& N. Hanrart including one folding view as frontispiece, original green pebbled cloth, gilt lettered direct, ruled in blind.
Not in Abbey; Mendelssohn (1957), p. 177.

Mendelssohn writes that the descriptive letterpress is ample and instructive, and gives, in the majority of instances, a complete history of each building depicted.

84

BURCHELL, WILLIAM JOHN.
Travels in the Interior of Southern Africa.
A. & R. Spottiswoode for Longman, Hurst, Rees, Orme
& Brown, 1822-24.

First edition. 2 vols., 4to, Vol. I. with errata slip Hints on
Emigration, 20 handcoloured aquatint plates after Burchell, 5
folding, folding engraved map, numerous woodengraved
illustrations, without half titles or blank in Vol. I, contemporary
half calf over marbled boards, preserved in 20th century
modern buckram box trimmed in morocco.
Abbey Travel I, 328; Gay 3001; Mendelssohn I, pg. 224;
Tooley 116.

"The most valuable and accurate work on South Africa
published up to the first quarter of the 19th century" –
Mendelssohn. Burchell set out from Cape Town in June
1811 on his travels in Africa, and covered four thousand
five hundred miles in the interior, returning to the Cape in
April 1815. He brought with him natural history
specimens and 500 drawings, some of which were
engraved to illustrate the present work. Some of the
panoramic views were executed on the then practically
unknown principle of scenographic projection on the
surface of a revoling cylinder… His account has been
described as "remarkable for the excellence of its literary
style and the fidelity of the numerous illustrations. A third
volume was projected but never published" DNB. As he
was accompanied only by natives many had thought his
venture unwise but it proved otherwise.

Plate IX.

19.

20.

Chase of the Hartebeest. H. B. 39.

BUTLER, Captain Henry.
South African Sketches: illustrative of the Wild Life of a Hunter on the Frontier of the Cape Colony. By Captain H. Butler, 59th Reg.
London, C. Wood, published by Ackermann & Co., 1841.

Folio, lithographed title, printed title, 15 plates (No. 1-15) with 31 lithographed views and vignettes (15 handcoloured).
Abbey Travel I, 336; Mendelssohn I. P. 235; Schwerdt I, p. 90; Tooley 126.

First edition of this rather scarce book (Mendelssohn) which describes the sporting adventures on the "Bontebok Flats" in Kaffraria, near the Kat River Settlement. Abbey Travel describes the work as "interesting".

Campbell del.,   Clark sculp.

Mahootoo, Queen of Lattakoo in full dress.

London, Pub.ᵈ by F. Westley, 10, Stationers Court, 1822.

CAMPBELL, Rev. John.
Travels in South Africa, undertaken at the request of the London Missionary Society, being a narrative of a second journey in the Interior of the country.
London, T. C. Hansard for the Society, published and sold by Francis Westley, 1822.

First edition. 2 vols., 8vo, half title, advertisements, handcoloured engraved folding map, 12 handcoloured aquatint plates by Clark after Campbell, slightly later half calf, spine flat and gilt.
Abbey Travel 328; Tooley 127; Mendelssohn I, p. 255.

Campbell's description of his second journey.

86

[DICKINSON, publisher]
Sketches of the Various Classes and Tribes Inhabiting the Colony of the Cape of Good Hope...
London, 1851.

Small 4to, lithographed frontispiece, and 41 lithographed plates all handcoloured, original cloth lettered in gilt on upper cover direct "The Caffre Tribes".
S.A. Bib. Vol. IV, p.220.

A scarce and interesting work on the Kaffirs, which is only listed in one bibliography and has only apparently come up at auction once in recent years. This copy is with a set of original watercolours for the work preserved in a modern folder, some of these are signed J.W. These watercolour costume plates have been attributed to Charles Bell (listed in Dictionary of South African Bibliography Vol. I, pp. 64/65) and it has been remarked that as there is some resemblance between finished watercolours of various South African nature types signed by or attributed to Bell and rather crude pictures of similar subjects marked J.W., students of Africana tend to believe that Bell produced the originals and that a lesser artist or artists made multiple copies for sale by the Cape Town booksellers, these being the basis for Sketches of some of the various classes and tribes inhabiting the Colony of the Cape of Good Hope published London 1851 (above).

In the absence of anything more positive it is suspected that Charles Bell himself was the artist of the sketches signed with the initials "J.W.", which may have been the entirely fictitious "smokescreen" initials of someone who acted as a go-between for Bell in the sale of his sketches. It is perhaps surprising that in such a small community as Cape Town was in the mid-19th century, that if there really had been an artist JW active over a period of ten or more years, absolutely nothing is known of him. He is so shadowy that I doubt his existence – and that leaves Charles Bell himself.

A second copy in original cloth of this scarce work is in this collection.

CHASSIRON, Charles de.
Apercu Pittoresque de la Regence de Tunis.
Paris, Imprimerie Bernard et Cie, 1849.

Oblong folio, 42 tinted lithographed plates, of which 8 plates of military subjects handcoloured, period style half calf gilt, label on upper cover.
Gay 1313 calls for only 37 plates on 42; Ashbee 225 (very scarce work).

The author was attached to the Embassy in Tunis in 1848. The plates were lithographed by Bichebois, Fichot, Bachelier, Deroy, Arnout Pere; Jules Arnout, Tirpenne and Bour after drawings by the author. They represent Tunis (panorama, lake and street), Bizerte, Carthage, Sousse, Kairouan, Mannam-Lif, Hammamet, Monastir, Mahdia, Zaghouan, costumes both civil and military, including, infantry, navy, a Muleteer; an Arab of Keff, a Rider for the Bey; a Janissary of the Divan; a Moorish girl; a Moorish interior; arms and instruments.

Presentation copy from the author to General Daumas, who was charged by General Bugeaud with native affairs in Algeria. Inscribed by the author on title page, with the General's ex libris beneath the imprint.

[COMBE, William.]
A History of Madeira with a Series of Twenty-Seven coloured Engravings, illustrative of the Costumes, Manners, and Occupations of the Inhabitants of that Island.
London, R. Ackermann, Printed by William Clowes, 1821.

Small 4to, title, preface, contents leaf, text pp. 1-118, 27 handcoloured aquatint plates, all vignetted, except for No. 27, calf-backed boards, marbled sides.
Abbey Travel 189; Tooley 150; Lipperheide 1581; Colas 1455; Gay 2979; Lipperheide 1581; Martin Hardie 113, 31.

Plates show life, occupations and pastimes of the inhabitants of the island.

CORRY, Joseph.
Observations upon the Windward Coast of Africa, the Religion, Character, Customs & c. of the Natives; with A System upon which they may be civilized, and a Knowledge Attained of the Interior of this Extraordinary Quarter of the Globe...Made in the Years 1805 and 1806...With an appendix containing a letter to Lord Howick, on the most simple and effectual means of abolishing the slave trade.
London, W. Bulmer & Co., for G.& W. Nichol and James Asperne, 1807.

First edition. 4to, half title, 8 handcoloured aquatint plates by J.C. Stadler, after drawings by R. Cocking after sketches by Corry, engraved map, 19th century sprinkled calf, spine raised bands, gilt ruled.
Abbey Travel 278; Gay 2857; Lowndes I, p. 527; not in Tooley.

This part of the West African coast was the centre of a busy slave trade, prospective owners in the New World could call on their agricultural knowledge. This work as well as showing the Africans in their villages, in their fields etc., introduces an appendix on the slave trade.

91 - 92

DANIELL, Samuel.
African Scenery and Animals at the Cape of Good Hope.
London, by the author, 1804.

3 parts in one, large oblong folio, mounted on guards, without text, 2 aquatint section titles, 30 fine handcoloured aquatint plates by Samuel and William Daniell, on thick paper, 19th century green morocco, ornate gilt borders, spine ornately gilt, raised bands.
Abbey Travel I, 321; Mendelssohn I, p. 411; Nissen ZBI 1035; Tooley 168.

"The scarcest and most valuable of the large atlas folios of South African illustration…a most magnificent work" (Mendelssohn). Samuel was the younger brother of William, nephew of Thomas Daniell. His interests of natural history and travel gained him a post in the Cape Colony soon after colonisation by the British. He was appointed secretary to Dundas and artist to Truter's expedition which in 1801 explored the region North and East of the Cape Colony now the Botswana borders, the area of the rivers Moloppo and Kuraman. Daniell himself discovered the source of the Kuraman river. He made numerous sketches which were used for this work and his Sketches representing the Native Tribes.

DANIELL, Samuel.
A Picturesque Illustration of the Scenery, Animals and Native Inhabitants of the Island of Ceylon.
London, T. Bensley, [1807]-1808.

Oblong folio, 11 handcoloured aquatint plates, 1 softground etching, contemporary green morocco, with the arms of Beriah Botfield in gilt on sides, from the Longleat Library sale.
Abbey Travel 410; Tooley 170; De Silva pp. 2-23.

Daniell produced an impressive body of work, amongst which, his views of Ceylon rate highly. Daniell arrived in Ceylon in 1805 aboard H.M.S. Greyhound. A protégé of the Governor, Sir Thomas Maitland, he was appointed Secretary to the Board of Revenue and Commerce in 1806. Concerning his art, Sutton writes that he was the most inspired and original of the three Daniell brothers and that his illustrations "are of such clarity and outstanding merit that they are sufficient to give a good idea of what Samuel might have achieved had he enjoyed a longer life." He writes of the Ceylon volume, "it would be difficult to make a choice of the masterpiece among these plates, but for sheer beauty that of the "Spotted Antelope" should be singled out for special praise: indeed, it must surely rank among the most lovely aquatints ever published. The superb drawing of the delicate animal, its beautiful colouring, its shy gentleness silhouetted against the brilliant light greens and the deep patches of darker foliage, combine with the composition of the picture to form an exquisite engraving of unforgettable charm…"

95

[DISTON, A.]
Costumes of the Canary Islands.
London, Smith, Elder and Co., 1829.

Part I (all published), 4to, title, text [6ll], 6 handcoloured lithographed plates on India paper, plates signed A. Diston del., and W. Fisk lith. Printed by W. Day, in original buff wrappers, title within lithographic border, preserved in 20th century green box.
Abbey Travel 75; not in Colas.

Plates include costumes and occupations. A series had been envisaged but this was to be the only part published, possibly due to the death of the author. The title to Part I refers to him as the late (Abbey).

ECKERSBERG, Johann F. and JOHNSON, James.
Views of the Island of Madiera.
Dusseldorf, Arnz & Comp. [c. 1850].

Oblong folio, 10 colour printed lithographed plates, some slight tinting, by Dr Franz Mittermaier after James Yale Johnson, original cloth, half straight grained morocco gilt, morocco lettering label on front cover.

Not in the normal bibliographies. Apparently a scarce work. Eckersberg is perhaps better known for his costumes of Norway listed in Colas.

[GRAHAM, Lieut. Sir Lumley and ROBINSON, Lieut. Hugh.]
Scenes in Kafirland, and Incidents in the Kafir War of 1851-2-3. From Sketches by two Officers of the 43rd Lt.-Infantry.
London, Messrs. Dickinson Bros., [1854].

Folio, letterpress title, 1p. explanatory text, 21 handcoloured lithographed plates by Dickinson Brothers after Graham or Robinson, on 18 leaves of thick wove paper, engraved subscription list, advertisement, later half morocco over brown cloth, spine gilt lettered direct.
Abbey Travel 344; S.A.Bib. Vol II, p.382; Mendelssohn I, p.801.

"The following sketches give some idea of the appearance and duties of the British soldier in Kafirland, as well of the enemy he has to contend with…It is hoped that these mountains and valleys will never again be the scene of strife, for they are far too beautiful to be invaded by sword and firebrand" (text leaf). It was Mendelssohn who succeeded in establishing the artists' names.

GRAMBERG, Jan Simon Gerardus.
Schetsen van Afrika's Westkust.
Amsterdam, Weijtingh & Brave, 1861.

First edition. 8vo, lithographed title with colour printed vignette, lithographed folding coloured frontispiece and 7 folding coloured plates, after Gramberg, and lithographed by C.C.A. Last, printed by H.L. van Hoogstraten, original brown cloth blocked in gilt and blind, spine gilt lettered direct.
Keynes Part I, Lot 323; otherwise not in usual bibliographies.

One of the illustrations after Gramberg for this work showed a factory on the slave coast (Gulf of Benin).

HARRIS, Sir William Cornwallis.
Portraits of the Game and Wild Animals of Southern Africa delineated from Life in their Native haunts, during a hunting expedition from the Cape Colony as far as the Tropic of Capricorn, in 1836 and 1837, with Sketches of the Field Sports.
London, H.W. Martin, published for the Proprietor by William Pickering, 1840-44. Dickinson and Son [1844].

Folio, 3pp. list of subscribers, lithographed coloured vignette title, printed title, (both dated 1840), 30 handcoloured lithographed plates, by Frank Howard after Harris, original buff wrappers dated 1841 for Parts 1-4, and for part 5, 1844, part numbers not indicated on wrappers, preserved in half burgundy box with marbled paper sides.
Abbey Travel 335; Schwerdt I, 231; Tooley 247; Mendelssohn, pp. 688-9.

"One of the most important and valuable works on South African Fauna" (Mendelssohn) The work was re-issued in 1844 by Richardson and again in 1849 by Bohn. Captain Harris, an officer in the East India Company's Bombay Engineers, was invalided to the Cape for two years, 1835-37. In 1836 he and Richard Williamson set off from Algoa Bay, by way of Somerset and the Orange River and travelled in a north-easterly direction until they reached the kraals of the famous Matabele chief Moselikatze. He proved friendly and allowed them to return by a hitherto closed route. This work was preceeded by an account of the journey published in Bombay in 1938 (8vo with a map and four plates). The response to this was so favourable that he was encouraged to publish the present work, based on his sketches of game animals. He was then sent to Shoa, Ethiopia, see work below, his success such that he was knighted. This collection also includes a Bohn edition of 1852 in 8vo with 26 coloured lithographed plates, which is not listed in Abbey, titled the Wild Sports of Southern Africa.

VIII. ACRONOTUS LUNATA:— THE SASSAYBE.

97

98

HARRIS, Sir William Cornwallis.
Illustrations of the Highlands of Aethiopia....on an Embassy to the Court of Shoa, in Southern Abyssinia. London, Dickinson and Son, [1844].

Folio, title, prefatory matter, 1 leaf, text descriptive of plates, 26ll., all versos blank, mounted lithographed frontispiece portrait of the author after O. Oakley, chromolithographed dedication to the Queen and 26 tinted lithographed plates after Martin Bernatz and the author, original blindstamped cloth, together with a separate suite of 28 additional handcoloured lithographed plates, each mounted on card within ruled border, loose as issued, preserved together in modern quarter brown morocco backed cloth box.
Abbey Travel I, 291.

A rare series of views. ABPC does not record a copy at auction since 1979. The series issued both with tinted lithographs and handcoloured as here. Harris's account of the embassy to the Court of Shoa was published in three vols. by Longman in the same year. Bernatz the artist attached to the expedition, himself brought out two vols. of views in 1852. The 3 vol. set with two tinted and one handcoloured lithographed frontispiece, folding engraved map.

JUNGMANN, R.
Costumes, Moeurs et Usages des Algeriens par R. Jungmann Refugie Polonais… Algeriens
Strasbourg, J. Bernard, 1837.

First edition. Oblong 4to, 84pp., 1 unn. Leaf (Vue d'Alger) lithographed by Simon Fils and Sandmann after Jungmann, 36 handcoloured lithographed plates numbered from plate 9-36, plate numbered 11-12 is a double page map of the kingdom of Algeria, contemporary morocco backed pebbled cloth, spine gilt in compartments, raised bands, dark red ruling, spine gilt in compartments, spine gilt lettered direct.
Colas 1581.

Colas quotes the Geng Library copy and adds that handcoloured copies as here are sometimes seen. An attractive collection of costume plates regarding Algeria.

LATROBE, Christian Ignatius.
Journal of a Visit to South Africa, in 1815, and 1816. With some accounts of the missionary settlements of the United Bretheren, near the Cape of Good Hope.

First edition. London, W. M'Dowall for L.B. Seeley and R. Ackermann, 1818. 4to, 2 pp. publishers advertisements, 16 plates, handcoloured aquatints except for one line engraving, from sketches by Latrobe or Mr. Melville, folding engraved map with routes marked in colours, uncut in modern red morocco, double gilt fillet, spine raised bands gilt, gilt ruled inner gilt dentelles by Zaehnsdorf.
Abbey Travel 325; Tooley 292; Mendelssohn I, pg. 866; Gay 3117.

Rare in this edition. Plates, which are signed drawn by R. Cocking, from the original Sketches of C. Latrobe. The plates were variously engraved by Stadler, Bluck, Havell, show views of Groenekloof and Gnadenthal and the mission house. Also views of Cape Town and Vicinity, the Mountains of Stellenbosch and start with views of St. Helena and the Ascension Island, obviously stopovers on the voyage to the Cape.

LEVAILLANT, Francois.
Second Voyage (de M. Le Vaillant) dans l'interieur de l'Afrique, par le Cap de Bonne-Esperance, dans les Annees 1783, 84 et 85.
Paris, Chez H.J. Jansen et Compte…[1795-6].

2 vols., 4to, 22 handcoloured engraved plates, five folding, contemporary mottled calf, single gilt fillet, spine flat and gilt in compartments.
Not in Abbey: see Nissen ZBI 2480; cf. Ronsil; Mendelssohn I, p. 889.

Levaillant's account of his first expedition through South Africa collecting botanical and zoological specimens.

Levaillant was born in Dutch Guiana in 1753 and after a European education he proceeded to Paris where he studied natural history. He became acquainted with Mr Temminck, Treasurer of the Dutch East India Company who enabled him to fulfil his ambition and make for the Cape. By the time he arrived for his first journey, war had broken out at the Cape. After some false starts due to the war, Levaillant was able to start preparing for his journey into the interior. In the meantime he extended his knowledge of the natural history and of the country with small excursions round the Cape. He travelled eventually to Blettenberg (Plettenberg), where he criticised the vanity of the Governor. This had not been his first complaint on the way. He had suggested that it was a nonsense to import timber into South Africa when the whole area was covered in forests (Mendelssohn).

LUCAS, Captain Thomas J.
Pen and Pencil Reminiscences of a Campaign in South Africa.
London, Day & Son [no date but 1861].

First edition. 4to, coloured lithographed title, frontispiece and 19 plates by Day & Son after Lucas.
Mendelssohn I, p. 932.

Light-hearted look at military and tribal life in South Africa. The author claims to amuse the reader rather than instruct, particularly his military friends from the Cape.

"Some little reminiscence of their sojourn in the country" (Preface).

LYON, Captain George Francis.
A Narrative of Travels in Northern Africa, in the Years 1818, 19, and 20; accompanied by geographical notices of the Soudan, and of the course of the Niger.
London, Thomas Davison for John Murray, 1821.

4to, folding engraved map, 17 handcoloured lithographed plates after Lyon, by M. Gauci, G. Harley or D. Dighton, a few woodengraved illustrations.
Abbey Travel I, 304; Blackmer 1044; Gay 2780; Tooley 311; Colas and Lipperheide for the French edition, see below.
Lyon was Commander of H.M.S. Hecla from 1821-23.

This copy accompanied with 13 handcoloured aquatint plates, proof before the letter, all but two with sepia duplicates in final states with captions, each plate, but one, with descriptive text in manuscript. The title and preface are also present in manuscript, the title giving the date and publication as London, J. Murray, 1821. Interestingly it would appear that Lyon proposed having the book's drawings aquatinted in the hope of having them published as a supplement to the narrative above. Also included is a letter from Lyon to John Murray, one leaf with manuscript on both sides, discussing the plates and their possible publication; Lyon lists 11 plates as engraved and not published, and 4 drawings. Items housed hinged to linen stubs in full green morocco box.

Lyon took part in the battle of Algiers in 1816. In 1818 when Mr Ritchie, secretary of the embassy at Paris, arrived on his way to Tripoli at the start of his travels in Africa in the interests of the government, Lyon volunteered to take the place of Captain Frederick Marryat, and joined Ritchie in Tripoli. He already had some knowledge of Arabic, and for the next four months studied assiduously, not only the language, but the religious and social forms of the Arabs. They reached Murzak, where both were taken ill, Ritchie not surviving. Without funds or stores and still very weak from his fever, Lyon pushed on towards the southern boundary of Fezzan, but was obliged to return to Tripoli. This work was an account of his journey, illustrated with colour plates of costumes, sports &c., from Lyon's own drawings (DNB). The work was translated into French by Edouard Gauttier, an associate of the Bibliotheque Royale and the publishers of the Biographie Universelle.

105

MARTENS, Henry.
[Kaffir War, 1845-1852].
London, Rudolph Ackermann, [1852-1854].

Oblong folio, 5 handcoloured aquatint plates by J. Harris after Martens mounted on guards, without title or text, the first and fourth plates backed onto card, others untrimmed, in modern half red morocco, single gilt fillet to sides.
Mendelssohn I, p. 986.

Fine series rarely found complete as here. Plates titled as follows: 1. The Conference at Block Drift, Kaffir Land Jany 30th 1846. Lt. Governor Col. Hare and the Kaffir Chief Sandilla before commencement of hostilities. 2. The Battle of Gwanga, Cape of Good Hope – June 8th 1846. 3. The Capture of Fort Armstrong, Kaffir Land Feby. 22nd 1851; 4. Attack of the Kaffirs on the Troops of the 74th Highlanders at Kroomie Forest. 5. South African Army…Crossing the Great Orange River, December 1852. (final print published 1854, others 1852)

106

O'NEILL, Thomas.
Sketches of African Scenery, from Zanzibar to the Victoria Nyanza, being a series of coloured lithographic pictures, from original sketches by the late Mr Thomas O'Neill, of the Victoria Nyanza mission of the Church Missionary Society.
London, printed by Vincent Brooks, Day & Son, published at Church Missionary House, 1878.

First edition. 4to, publishers advertisements, 2 uncoloured illustrations, 19 chromolithographed views by Vincent Brooks, Day & Son after O'Neill, on 9 leaves (one double page), original lithographed wrappers within ornate borders incorporating flowers, elephant's tusks etc. preserved in modern red morocco backed cloth box, spine gilt raised bands.
Not in Abbey; Mendelssohn II, p. 271 refers to the item below.

Apparently a scarce work. Again interestingly produced by a member of the Church Missionary Society. The church playing an important part in the Colonial life in Africa.

HOTTENTOT GIRL.

Publ. May 10.1822. by Edw.d Orme, London.

107

ORME, Edward, publisher.
Collection of Portraits of the Savage Tribes inhabiting the Boundaries of the Colony of the Cape of Good Hope: taken from Life in 1812, by an Officer of the 21st Lt. Dragoons, engaged in an Expedition against those Tribes, under Lt.-Col. Graham (see above).
London, Edward Orme, printed at McQueen & Co.'s Lithog. Press, 1822.

2 vols., folio, lithographed title, 8 handcoloured lithographed portraits comprising 1. Hottentot woman. 2. A Kaffir Chief. 3. A Young Hottentot 4. A Bosheman 5. Hottentot Girl 6.Young Bosheman. 7. Female Hottentot with Child and 8. A Bosheman with Poisoned Arrows., four of these are lithographed by McQueen & Co., and four handcoloured aquatints.
Mendelssohn II, p.271.

Edward Orme was, after Rudolph Ackermann, the most important publisher of illustrated books during the short golden age of the coloured aquatint, and there is no evidence that he followed Ackermann's move into lithography. His total output totalled some 700 illustrations, but his monument is his British Field Sports of 1807, described by C.F.G.R. Schwerdt (1928) as "the finest and most important sporting book of the last two centuries." (See elsewhere in this catalogue). Mendelssohn's copy of Collection of Plates had plates in two states, uncoloured and coloured. He describes the latter as very rare. The work does appear in any case to be of the greatest rarity. The Keynes copy which appeared recently had six plates only of eight.

108

POCOCK, Lieut. W. Innes.
Five Views of the Island of St. Helena, from Drawings Taken on the Spot: to which is added a concise account of the island.
London, printed by D.N. Shury, published by S. & J. Fuller, 1815.

Oblong folio, one page subscription list, 5 handcoloured aquatint plates by T. Sutherland after Pocock, one double page, original boards with original printed label laid down on upper cover, cloth backed.
Abbey Travel I, 310; Tooley 381.

Very rare, no copies are listed as having sold at auction in the past twenty-five years before the Keynes sale 7th April 2004. The subscription list was limited to 58 copies. The author was the second son of renowned marine artist, Nicholas Pocock. The text makes clear that this was published in an attempt to satisfy public interest in the island, chosen by the allies to be the residence of Emperor Napoleon in exile.

108A

POCOCK, Lieut. William. Innes.
Historical Notices Relative to the Ancient and Modern
State of the Country and City of Algier; with an Account
of the Battle of the 27th August 1817.
[London] Published for the Proprietor by Messrs. Cadell
& Davies, 1817.

Oblong folio, drophead title, no preliminaries, starts at
gathering B, 3 handcoloured aquatint plates and one map, text
and plates stitched together and preserved in modern gray
cloth covered box, morocco label on upper cover.
Not in Abbey or Tooley.

Nicholas Pocock served mainly in the East and West Indies,
and made several voyages to the Cape of Good Hope, St.
Helena and China.

109

RAFFEREL, Anne.
Voyage dans l'Afrique Occidentale.
Paris, Arthus Bertrand, 1846.

2 vols., 8vo, text and 4to (latter atlas vol.), 11 handcoloured lithographed plates, two folding maps, lithographed after Rafferel by Kaeppelin in modern morocco backed boards spine in style of text volume.

AFRICAN MINSTRELS.

RAMSAY, T.W.
Costumes of the Western Coast of Africa. By an Officer of
the Commissariat.
[1833]

4to, lacking title, 6 handcoloured aquatint plates, original
printed wrappers.
Not in Abbey, Colas and one copy only cited in NUC.

An apparently scarce set of plates.

[ROUBAUD, Benjamin.]
Souvenirs d'Afrique Costumes francais et indigenes,
Scenes et Moeurs.
Gihaut Freres, Paris, [1846].

First editon. Oblong folio, 14 handcoloured lithographed plates
printed in colours and finished by hand by Auguste Bry after
sketches by the author, each image captioned in the plate, title
within decorative border to upper cover, publisher's catalogue
of list of books for sale relating to Algeria inside rear cover.
Bay 877bis; Colas 2581.

This copy has 14 lithographed plates as opposed to the 8
listed by Colas and there is a slight difference in the first
word of the title. It would seem in any case that the work
is of great rarity. Each of the plates listed in Colas carry
imprint Souvenirs d'Afrique par B. Roubaud. Their
cataloguer says that he has never seen any additional plates
from his list.

SALT, Sir Henry.
Twenty-Four Views in St. Helena, The Cape, India…
London, William Mitler, 1809.

Large oblong folio, 25 handcoloured aquatint plates, unfolded in early 19th century marbled boards, dark red morocco ruled borders, single gilt fillet and ornate outer gilt border.
Abbey Travel 515; Tooley 440.

In 1802 Salt left London for an eastern tour with George, Viscount Valentia (later Lord Mountnorris) whom he accompanied as secretary and draughtsman. He visited India, Ceylon, and in 1805 Abyssinia, returning to England in 1806. He made many drawings, some of which served to illustrate Lord Valentia's Voyages and Travels to India of 1809 and "Twenty-Four Views in St. Helena…and Egypt" which were both published by Salt from his own drawings in the same year. The originals of all these drawings were retained by Lord Valentia (DNB).

SEALE, Robert F.

The Geognosy of the Island of St. Helena, illustrated in a series of views, plans and sections; accompanied with explanatory remarks and observation.
London, Sedding & Turle for Ackermann & Co., 1834.

First edition. Oblong folio, title, verso blank; dedication, verso blank; list of subscribers (55 subscribers for 104 copies), 1 leaf, verso with list of plates; text, pages (7) to 25, 11 full page lithographed plates after Seale, drawn on stone by M. Gauci, printed by Graf & Soret, all coloured by hand, 8 unsigned coloured lithographed illustrations in the text, 4 handcoloured, 2 tinted by hand, original cloth with contemporary half morocco gilt ruled, upper cover gilt lettered, rebacked in modern cloth box.
Abbey Travel I, 317; BM(NH) IV, p.1889.

Magnificent illustrations of the extraordinary geology of St Helena. Seale was born on the island and later in the employ of the East India Company worked under Henry Brooke, perhaps the island's best known historian. In 1836 he was appointed first Colonial Secretary under the Crown, but was dismissed in 1838 and died suddenly in the following year. 104 copies were subscribed, of which the East India Company dedicatees ordered 40 copies

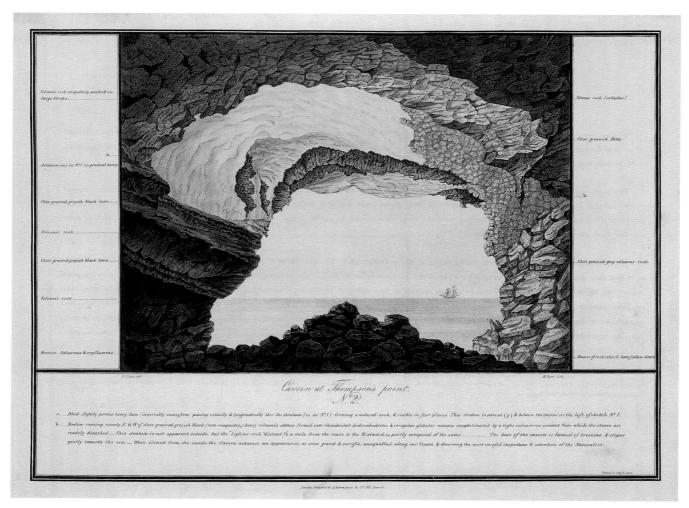

114

114
STACK, Lieut. Frederick Rice.
Souvenir of the Emperor Napoleon: consisting of six drawings made in the Island of St. Helena.
London and Paris: E. Bambart [and others], [1859]

Folio, lithographic dedication, 6 numbered hand-coloured lithographic plates by Charles Haghe after Stack, printed by Day and Son, plates bearing the imprint Chas. Haghe lith., captions in English and French, plates on guards in original cloth.
Abbey Travel I, 319.

Large paper copy with handcoloured plates. The Abbey copy is on ordinary paper with tinted plates. A series of views of Napoleon's residences on St. Helena by an army officer, drawn thirty years after the Emperor's death, and aimed at the French as much as the English market. The text is by Mrs Ward who identifies herself in the preface as a resident of the island from 1836 to 1839. Charles Haghe was Louis Haghe's younger brother, who worked with him over the years.

TEMPLE, Lieut. Richard.
Sixteen Views of Places in the Persian Gulf taken in the Years 1809-1810 illustrative of the proceedings of the forces employed on the expedition sent from Bombay, under the command of Capt. Wainwright of H.M. Ship Chiffone, and Lieut. Col. L. Smith & the Officers of H.M. 65th Regiment...
Bombay, 1813 but published by W. Haines, London, in that year.

First edition. Oblong folio, engraved title, 16 handcoloured aquatint plates, (complete as issued), all window mounted and preserved in modern red morocco album. Temple's second work on Mauritius listed in the India/ Indian Ocean section is uniformly bound with this. This with small 4to text vol. in blue wrappers, tipped into modern period style half red morocco gilt, spine gilt, raised bands.
Abbey Travel 389; Tooley 482; Ogilby Trust 905; Kelly Britain and the Gulf, 1795-1880 (for background information).

"The only colour plate book on the Persian Gulf and one of the rarest of all colour plate books". The dominant naval presence in the Persian Gulf were the Qawasin who had frequently attacked the British ships, culminating in the taking of Sylph. This, plus a fear of the Wahabis gaining control of Muscat at the expense of Saiyid Sa'id prompted the British to send in a formidable naval force to the Gulf to destroy Qawasin vessels. At this time Minto was Governor General of India and he commented of this campaign that "it had given him a glimpse of the illimitable consequence of taking sides in an intra-Muslim/intra Arab contest and the experience bought of prudence" (Kelly).

TULLY, [Miss].
Narrative of a Ten Years' Residence in Tripoli in Africa;…also an Account of the Domestic Manners of the Moors, Arabs, and Turks.
London, Henry Colburn, 1817.

Second edition. Small 4to, xii, [2] 376pp., 7 handcoloured aquatint plates, engraved folding map, modern half red morocco, ruled in black raised bands to sides.
Abbey Travel 301; Blackmer 1682.

Miss Tully was either the sister or sister in law of Richard Tully, Consul in Tripoli from 1783-1793. The work is particularly interesting for details of the domestic life of the Harem.

WATHEN, James.
A Series of Views Illustrative of St. Helena.
London, for the Proprietor T. Clay, Robert Jennings and John Major, September 1821.

First edition. 4to, proof portrait of Wathen after A.J. Oliver, engraved title with handcoloured aquatint vignette and 9 handcoloured aquatint plates after Wathen by I. Clark, "arranged by E.W.", numbered 2-10, one doublepage, 2 woodengraved tailpieces, plates in two states, 30 uncoloured proofs on India proof paper at rear, original wrappers, preserved in 20th century half calf, spine gilt lettered direct, half morocco over marbled boards.
Abbey Travel 314; not in Tooley.

This collection includes a second copy of the work in original printed wrappers.

The artist went on frequent walking excursions throughout Great Britain and Ireland, his regular contributions to the Gentleman's Magazine earning him the sobriquet of "Jemmy Sketch". As the advertisement to this volume states, he spent "not quite three days" on St. Helena in the summer of 1812, making "no fewer than 13 drawings, two of which were published in his Journal of a Voyage to Madras and China of 1811 and eight of which appear here. Two other sketches, the View of Longwood and title vignette of Napoleon's tomb, are "the result of a later performance". Abbey notes that the portrait does not appear in all copies.

Levant and Ottoman Empire

ARIF PASHA, Muchir.
Les Anciens Costumes de l'Empire Ottoman depuis l'Origine de la Monarchie jusqu'a la Reforme du Sultan Mahmoud Recueillis par S. Ex. Le Muchir Arif Pacha, [1863].

First edition. 2 parts in one vol., folio, 47pp., [16], p1. first page of French text, pp. [1-16 text in Turkish], text within double rules, lithographed title on stiff paper, printed in sepia, lithographed portrait and 16 lithographed plates with hand colouring, full polished calf, upper cover panelled in blind with elaborate arabesques.
BL; GL; Colas 148 gives the date as [1864]; Blackmer 43, without Turkish letterpress. The title of the Blackmer copy is taken from the wrapper, V & A.

This edition with text in Turkish and French. The date 1272 is in Arabic letter on the title. This work was published in both coloured and uncoloured formats, although the black and white format probably had plates tinted in one colour. The author fought against the Greeks in Athens and Euyboea from 1826-28 and then in the Syrian campaigns against Mehmet Ali. He became governor of the province of Silistria and while there prepared this work for publication. The plates contain 80 figures of Ottoman functionaries whose duties are explained in the text.

BARKER, Henry Aston.

A Series of Eight Views, Forming a Panorama of the Celebrated City of Constantinople and its Environs, taken from the Town of Galata, by Henry Aston Barker and exhibited in his Great Rotunda, Leicester Square.
[London], Thomas Palser...and Henry Aston Barker...
Printed by George Smeeton, January 1st, 1813.

First and only edition. Large folio, no letterpress, engraved title leaf, and 8 separate aquatinted plates, with panorama key in the round, handcoloured and preserved in modern half red morocco, label in gilt, a scarce work.
Not in BLC; GL, plates only; Blackmer 76; Atabey 60, title and key in facsimile.

The title and key plate are both rarely present. The drawings for the panorama were taken on the spot. Barker set out on extended travels in Europe and the Levant in 1799. The panorama of Constantinople was constructed and exhibited at the Panorama, Leicester Square, in 1801, which he managed with his father, Robert Barker. He later worked with John Burford at the Panorama, Strand, constructing panoramas of cities he had visited in the Levant, including Athens and Corfu.

BELZONI, Giovanni Battista.

Narrative of the Operations and Recent Discoveries within the Pyramids, Temples, Tombs, and Excavations, In Egypt and Nubia; and of a Journey to the Coast of the Red Sea, In Search of the Ancient Berenice; And another to the Oasis of Jupiter Ammon...
London, John Murray, 1820.

First edition. 2 vols., 4to and large oblong folio, first vol. title and text, portrait frontispiece of Belzoni, 44 plates on 34 sheets of which 19 handcoloured lithographs, the remaining 25 plates are engravings of which 21 handcoloured, contemporary half green morocco, gilt ruled over marbled boards, spine raised bands, gilt ruled.
Blackmer 116; not in Abbey Travel and this edition not in Atabey.

The second and third editions to this work followed in 1821 and 1822. Some copies of the first edition text contain an 'Appendix' by Thomas Young. Belzoni was one of the most interesting figures in the history of eastern travel (DNB) and certainly next to Burckhardt, the most interesting in the history of Egyptology and Egyptian travel. He had been a strong man in the circus and had studied hydraulics in Rome. In 1815 he went to Egypt with the idea of offering his services to Mehmet Ali in producing a machine to aid in irrigation but the idea failed. Burckhardt suggested to Henry Salt that Belzoni should attempt to move the head of Memnon (Rhamses II)

from Thebes to Cairo. This was carried out successfully in 1816. Inspite of a lack of knowledge Belzoni began his remarkable career as an archaeologist, still working for Salt, removing an amazing number of Sarcophagi and statues. In 1817 he excavated Abu Simbel, Karnak and the Valley of the Kings, and the tomb of Seti I, whose sarcophagus was purchased by Sir John Soane. In 1818 he opened the second pyramid at Gizeh and identified the site of Berenice. In 1819 he left Egypt for England where he undertook the production of his book and organised an exhibition of his Egyptian antiquities. His collection was sold by Sotheby's in 1822. Sarah Belzoni contributed some drawings to the work. This was the first English work of any consequence to use lithography (Blackmer).

FROM THE KINGS TOMBS IN THEBES
London. Published by John Murray Albemarle Street 1820.

BRINDESI, Jean.
Elbicei Atika, Musee des Anciens Costumes Turcs de Constantinople.
Paris, Lemercier, [c. 1855].

First edition. Large Folio, without text as issued, chromolithographed title and 22 lithographed plates printed in colour with some heightening by hand, original cloth covers stamped in blind and gilt, this with later quarter green morocco to strengthen.
GL; not in BL, nor Weber or Abbey. V&A; Colas 446 attributes the date to 1855.

Elbicei Atika was the name of the costume museum in Istanbul. Murray's Guide to Turkey, 1854, describes it. The collection of plates depicts the costume of the Ottoman court. Although Brindesi's work has not been reprinted, it has reappeared in other forms, including an album of early photographs made from these plates now in the Gennadius Library. Born in Constantinople and a pupil of M. Porfirio Giulani he painted many watercolours of the city as well as this lithographed costume work and a second lithographed work comprising views of the Ottoman capital (see below).
Colas suggests this work formed part of a collection published by Collinot and Beaumont under a general title "Encyclopedie des Arts Decoratifs de l'Orient".[c.1880]. This is in fact not the case. The Encyclopedie consisted of six original parts containing ornaments and decoration from Persia, Arabia, Turkey, Japan, China and Venice, plus two supplementary works by Preziosi on Constantinople and Cairo.

BRINDESI, Jean.
Souvenirs de Constantinople.
Paris, Lemercier, [c. 1855].

First and apparently only edition. Oblong folio, printed title, 20 lithographed plates printed in colours, original cloth gilt, upper cover blindstamped with gilt cartouching.
Blackmer 207; Atabey 152; Colas 447; not in Abbey. V&A.

Colas calls for 21 plates, but no such copy has been seen. The plates are scenes of life on the Bosphorus and in Constantinople, including the Sweet Waters of Asia, the Bazaars, the Saint Sophia, a view from the residence of the artist in Pera and others.

123
[CARTWRIGHT, Joseph.
Views in the Ionian Islands.
London, [G. Havell], 1821.]

First edition. Large folio, dedication verso blank, text, 3 leaves versos blank, 12 handcoloured aquatint plates, mounted on card in imitation of drawings, all mounts tinted light grey on upper surface, plates without titles, signed Cartwright del. Eng. & Col. R. Havell & Co., titles taken from the text, half black straight-grained morocco gilt over cloth, upper cover gilt lettered, from the Liverpool Free Public Library.
Abbey Travel 134; Tooley 132; Droulia 119; not in Blackmer, Atabey, nor Legrand or 132; Pernot.

Tooley in his collation suggests that there was a separate title page, but this was almost certainly not the case. Joseph Cartwright was appointed Paymaster General of the Forces at Corfu when the Ionian Islands came into British possession. The present volume was published soon after he returned to England, probably appearing in 1821. The following year he produced a book of Albanian and Greek costumes and thereafter concentrated on marine paintings (Abbey).

126

COLE, William.
Select Views of the Remains of Ancient Monuments In Greece, As At Present Existing, from drawings Taken and Coloured on the Spot In The Year 1833.
London, for the Author. By Ackermann and Co., 1835.

First edition. Folio, subscribers list, 12 handcoloured sepia mounted aquatint plates, loose as issued in original wrappers and preserved in linen covered box, label on spine, gilt lettered. Abbey Travel 132 for a coloured copy; not in Tooley; Blackmer 77, but not in Atabey; BL; GL; Weber 1123 calls for a frontispiece in error.

The author was an architect from the Wirral, practising particularly in Chester and Birkenhead, specialising in municipal buildings. He was in Athens in 1833. It was at this time that many of the ancient monuments there had been cleared of the modern buildings which concealed them and was an important opportunity for recording the antiquities.

127

COSTUME. RECUEIL DES DIFFERENS COSTUMES
des principaux Officiers et Magistrats de la Porte; et des peoples sujets de l'Empire Othoman, tels que les Grecs, les Armeniens, les Arabes, les Egyptiens, les Macedoniens, les Juifs &c. On y joint une courte explication des usages, moeurs, coutumes et religion, de ces diverses nations, tiree des meilleurs auteurs.
Paris, Chez Onfroy Libraire Quay des Augustins au Lys d'Or, [1775].

First and only edition. Folio, title page, one leaf index of plates, 16 leaves of text, all engraved within gilt ruled borders, title border handcoloured, 96 engraved plates, handcoloured, all within borders after Matth. Wolfgang Vindel by Jeremiah Wolff, morocco backed boards.

GL (for incomplete copy); not in Weber; BL or Cohen de Ricci; Colas 2501 (he was unable to see a copy, most known copies apparently uncoloured); Blackmer 1399;

Publisher Onfroy perhaps the Editor, some plates identify the artist and engraver as Pitre and Juillet respectively. The plates depict the costume of the Ottoman court and military functionaries in detail and also those of the "fourteen nations". Approximately a third of the work is based on prototypes from Nicolay's 16th century work, famously repeated and enlarged in Chalcondyles. Some of these have been retitled.

124

[CLARK, I. H., artist.]
The Military Costume of Turkey.
London, Thomas McLean, 1802.

Small folio, dedication, preface, contents, etched handcoloured; portrait frontispiece by and after Wageman, vignette title, 30 handcoloured plates, all aquatinted, contemporary brown morocco.

Abbey Travel 373 for a later edition of 1818 which may have been prepared for inclusion in Miller's series of costume books.

125

CLERGET, L.
Souvenirs de Jerusalem.
Paris, Arthus Bernard, [1861].

First and only edition. Large folio, lithographed plan of Saint Sepulchre on title, 14 lithographed plates by Clerget, Bachelier, Guildrou, and Fichot, of which 12 coloured and two tinted, 6 leaves of text, contemporary green morocco triple gilt borders surrounding gilt titling.
BL; GL; Blackmer 1255; Tobler 231; not in Abbey; Weber 1181.

Most of the plates illustrate various parts of the church of the Holy Sepulchre. Paris was named commander of the third division of the Mediterranean squadron in the third division of the Mediterranean squadron in December, 1858. He was already known as a naval artist, and he produced works on the technology of steam engines and other technical matters. A pictorial account of the French Mediterranean squadron's visit to Jerusalem in 1861.

Le Mousti Commandant des Mosquée Officier du Divan.

Il y a Chez les Turcs deux sortes de Divan, le Premier est publique et tout le monde a le droit de s'y presenter, pour y plaider sa cause. Il se tient dans une Grande Salle du Palais du Grand Visir, qui est obligé de rendre la justice au Peuple quatre fois la Semaine, le Lundi, le Mercredi, le Vendredi et le Samedi. la Justice se rend promptement et elle est sans Appel. On puniroit de la bastonnade celui qui par ses Conseils, par Obstinations, ou par Interêt, voudroit embrouiller une affaire. Le Divan doit se tenir jusqu'à la fin du Jour, a moins qu'il n'y est plus de Cause a juger. Les Juges dinent dans cette Salle, et leur repas ne dure qu'une demi heure. L'autre Divan est surnommé Gallibé, ou Conseil privé du Grand Seigneur, Il se tient les Dimanches et les Mardis. On y traite des affaires politiques, de ce qui concerne les forces de terre, de Mer, en un mot de tout ce qui a rapport à l'Etat,

DALLAWAY, James.

Constantinople Ancient and Modern, with Excursions to the Shores and Islands of the Archipelago and to the Troad.

London, T. Bensley, 1797.

First edition. 4to, engraved title, 9 handcoloured aquatint plates, large paper copy, engraved map, contemporary calf.
Abbey Travel 392; Blackmer 441; Atabey 308; Prideaux 223.

A few copies only of this work appeared on large paper with plates handcoloured as here. Dallaway travelled to Constantinople as Chaplain to Liston's embassy to the Porte. Gaetano Mercati, who produced the drawings for this work was Liston's draughtsman. Dallaway spent eighteen months in Constantinople and travelled to the Troad. Mercati was aulmoner and physician to the English embassy (Hitzel).

DALTON, Richard.

Antiquities and Views in Greece and Egypt with the Manners and Customs of the Inhabitants From Drawings made on the Spot A.D. 1749.

[London], Thomas King and Henry Chapman, 1791.

First collected edition. Large folio, [1] 12, 79 engraved plates on 76 sheets, of which 6 double-page, by Chatelain, Vivares, Rooker, Basire, Mason &c, 27 costume plates handcoloured, later half red morocco, over marbled boards, spine ornately gilt in compartments, raised bands.
BL; Weber 825; Blackmer 443; Colas 779; Atabey 311.

This edition has the series costume plates, displayed two to a page not present in the earlier edition. Over the years Dalton made arrangements himself to have the sketches he had made during his tour of the Levant with James Caulfield, the Earl of Charlemont's party in 1749-50. This work appeared in four stages, the 23 plates of Athens were engraved in 1751, the 20 plates of Egypt, Aetna and the Archipelago appeared in 1752, the nine plates of Halicarnassus [present day Bodrum] were engraved by Dalton sometime after 1771, and the 21 plates of Egypt were engraved in 1781, together with the six costume portraits, each printed on a separate sheet, in this 1791 edition, the only one with a general title page, these six plates are printed two to a page. All copies seem to have been uncoloured. For Lord Charlemont's journey, see W. Standford and E.J. Finopoulos. The Travels of Lord Charlemont in Greece and Turkey, London, 1984.

The Basso Relievos on the Frize of the Inner Portico of the Temple of Minerva | *Les Bas Reliefs de la Frise du*

DALVIMART, Octavien.

The Costume of Turkey, Illustrated by a Series of Engravings; with Descriptions in English and French.
London, for William Miller, 1802.

Folio, 60 no'ed handcoloured aquatint plates, later half red morocco over marbled boards, spine ornately gilt in compartments raised band.
Abbey Travel 370 for the 1804 edition.

Atabey states that this is the true first edition with the colouring more detailed, especially on the title vignette. This work has several times been reprinted using the same plates and text.

Octavien Dalvimart Delin.

Dadley, Sculp.t

Publish'd January 1.1802. by W. Miller, Old Bond Str.t London.

Intérieure du Temple de Minerve.

DAVENPORT, W.

Historical Portraiture of Leading Events in the Life of Ali Pacha.
London, T. M'Lean, 1823.

First and apparently only edition. Small folio, 30pp., [2], 6 handcoloured aquatint plates, engraved by G. Hunt, 20th century half red morocco, leather label gilt lettered upper cover, spine raised bands, gilt lettered, g.e.
Abbey Travel 206; Tooley 179; Atabey 325; Blackmer 441.

The text is taken from the English edition of the Life of Ali Pasha by Beauchamp. The author may be connected with the R.A. Davenport who produced a biography of Ali in 1837 (Atabey).

DAVYDOF, Vladimir P.

Atlas'K Putevym Zapiskam Davidova, po Unicheskim, Ostrovam, Gretsii, Maloj Azii I Turtsii [Views in the Ionian Islands, Greece and Asia Minor].
St. Petersburg, Latronne for Fisher, 1840.

First edition. Folio, text in Russian, vignette title, by Benoit after Wolfensberger, 33 handcoloured lithographed plates, 5 double page and folding, various sizes, some captioned in French and English, II, engraved plates partially coloured, by Jacottet, Villneuve, Julien, Sabatier, Benoit, Schvekhten, P. Razumikhin, Vogel, Salathe, Hibon, Guiaud, Bichebois, after Bryulov, Efimov, J.J. Wolfensberger, and Berlin neo-classical architect, Karl Friedrich Schinkel, loose in original printed wrappers, in contemporary cloth cover, original printed paper label on upper cover, preserved in modern half green morocco over cloth box, green labelling piece gilt on upper cover. Not in Abbey nor Weber; Blackmer 461.

This outstanding set of views of Greece and Turkey, rarely found complete as here, combines the techniques of aquatint and lithography. The aquatinted base giving a depth, whilst complementing the freedom of lithography. Bryulov and Efimov travelled with Davydof. Most of the plates are after artists Bryulov and Swiss artist J.J. Wolfensberger. The text does not mention Wolfensberger as a member of the group travelling with Davydof, so he must have had access to his drawings in some way. Plates include architectural plans of the churches in Constantinople and Mt Athos by architect Efimov, and of the Parthenon by Bryullov. The plates were in fact printed by Letronne in Paris.

133

[DEVAL, Charles].
Deux Annees a Constantinople et en Moree (1825-26)
ou Esquisses Historiques sur Mahmoud, les Janissaires,
les nouvelles troupes, Ibrahim-Pacha, Solyman-Bey etc...
London, R.G. Jones, [and] Paris, Nepveu, 1828.

Second edition. 8vo., [iv], 219pp., 16 handcoloured lithographed
plates by Langlume after Collin, handcoloured and heightened
with gold, green calf backed boards, spines flat and gilt.
Colas 853; Blackmer 480; Loukia Droulia 1481; Atabey 347.

The very scarce first edition appeared in 1827. Deval, a
native of Constantinople, was attached to the French
Embassy of Andreossy as an interpreter. Deval had studied
at the interpreters' school in Constantinople in 1825-26.

134

DEVEREUX, W.B.
Views on the Shores of the Mediterranean.
London, Dickinson & Co., 1847.

First and only edition. Large folio, lithographed dedication to
Queen Victoria, 24 lithographed plates, of which 20
handcoloured, half brown morocco over cloth gilt.
Blackmer 482; not in Abbey; Tooley, Atabey or V & A.

This work is found with tinted plates only, but irrespective
of colouring there do seem to have been two issues.
Unusual sites are illustrated here, mostly in Greece and
Asia Minor. In 1844 Devereux, captain of the sloop Snake,
assisted a Mr Alison of the British embassy at
Constantinople to examine the sculptures of the castle at
Bodrum. The drawings of the bas-reliefs in plates 15-18
were made at that time. Other plates are of Corfu, Delos,
Athens, Mount Olympus Philippi, the Troad, Ephesus,
Bethlehem and Carthage.

135

136

DODWELL, Edward.
A Classical and Topographical Tour through Greece, during the Years 1801, 1805, and 1806.
London, Rodwell and Martin, 1819.

First edition. 2 vols., 4to, folding map and 66 engraved plates, of which 6 double-page, contemporary morocco gilt, ruled border, spine gilt in compartments, sides gilt ruled, m.e.
Not in Abbey or Tooley, but see Abbey Travel 130 for description of folio plates by Dodwell; Atabey 356; Weber 62; Blackmer 492.

Dodwell made two trips to Greece, in 1801 to the Troad and Ionian Islands with William Gell, and then more extensively in 1805-06 when on parole as a French prisoner in company with the artist Simone Pomardi. Most of the plates are engraved after Pomardi's drawings, which he made into a much scarcer work describing this journey entitled, Viaggio nella Grecia, 1820.

136

DODWELL, Edward.
Views in Greece from Drawings by Edward Dodwell, Esq., F.S.A.
London, Rodwell and Martin, 1821.

Large Folio, [vi], [60], 30 handcoloured aquatinted plates, mounted on card with captions on verso of each plate, contemporary red straight-grained morocco, panelled and gilt, elaborate blind and gilt borders and fillets, spine gilt in compartments, fan device gilt in each corner, g.e.
BL; Weber 1110; Blackmer 493; Atabey 357; Abbey 130; Colas 875.

These illustrations had been intended for the account of Dodwell's travels, but the cost proved prohibitive, so thirty illustrations were selected to appear separately. A second edition appeared in 1830 with one additional plate. This work was remaindered in about 1823 by Priestley & Weale and offered for sale half bound.

136

NICOLACKI MITROPOLOS,

arborant l'étendard de la Croix à Salona, le jour de Pâques 1821.

DUPRE, Louis.

Voyage a Athenes et a Constantinople, ou Collection de Portraits, de Vues et de Costumes Grecs et Ottomans, peints sur les lieux, d'après la nature, lithographies et colories par L. Dupre, eleve de David; Accompagne d'un texte orne de vignettes.
Paris, H. Gache, Imprimerie de Dondey-Dupre, 1825.

First edition. Large folio, 40 handcoloured lithographed plates by and after Dupre, and a double-page engraved plate of a Turkish passport, 12 vignettes in the letterpress, contemporary morocco backed marbled boards, initials J.P. at base of spine. BL; GL (leaf to binders; Atabey 381; BN; Weber 130; Colas 916; not in Abbey.)

Dupre had been a pupil in David's studio. Recommended by Cardinal Fesch in 1811, Dupre became official court painter at Kassel to King Jerome of Westphalia. He obtained a pension to live in Italy and divided his time between Naples and Rome from 1814. In 1819 he managed to make a six month journey to Greece and Constantinople, where he stayed for three months. He was guided in his work by M. Jouannin, the senior interpreter to the French Embassy, who introduced him to Greek Princes and rich Armenian families, notably the family of the Duzoglou, the leading jewellers and silversmiths to the Court (Hitzel). Most of the fine portraits were of the people Dupre met during his journey and the fine colouring of the plates is said to be due to Dupre himself. The plates include a Turk and young Greek against a background of the fortress of Janina. A "tirage apart" was made of the 12 vignettes and was published under the title, Album Grec, undated but printed in Paris by Thierry Freres.

DURAND-BRAGER, Jean Baptiste Henri.

A Voyage in the Black Sea, the Bosphorus, the Sea of Marmora and the Dardanelles...
London, P. & B.D. Colnaghi...; Eug. Gambart & Co., Paris, Lemercier, [c.1855].

First and apparently only edition. Oblong folio, title and list of plates, without text as issued, 24 handcoloured numbered lithographed plates, after the author by Sabatier, Eug. Ciceri et Ph. Benoist, preserved in modern cloth covered box, black morocco labelling piece, gilt, similar on spine.
Blackmer 520; Atabey 383; not in Abbey Travel

A scarce work, particularly coloured as here. The marine artist Durand-Brager was attached to the French squadron in the Black Sea during the Crimean War. He was charged especially with the task of taking plans of the Russian fortresses and taking views of the coasts for purposes of navigation. According to Bazencourt his plans and drawings were lithographed at the French Ministry of the Marine, at the depot for maps and plans. Frederic Hitzel writes that Durand Brager contributed to Le Monde Illustre and L'Illustration under his own name and to La Patrie under a pseudonym Rambal, both illustrated French newspapers were published during the Crimean War. In 1852 he had travelled to St. Helena as the official artist with the expedition commissioned to return Napoleon Bonaparte's ashes to France. He had been a pupil of Theodore Gudin and Eugene Isabey and his career flourished under the July Monarchy and the Second Empire. He exhibited three paintings of the Bosphorus and Constantinople at the Salons in 1861 From the Hofbibliothek zu Donaueschingen.

139

140

FERRIOL, Charles de, Marquis.
Recueil de Cent Estampes representant differentes Nations du Levant, Gravees sur les Tableaux Peints d'apres Nature en 1707 & 1708. Par les Ordres de M. de Ferriol...Et mis au jour en 1712 & 1713. Par les Soins de M. Le Hay.
Paris, Chez Basan Graveur avec Privilege du Roi, 1714.

Second edition. Folio, no letterpress but with engraved title and seven leaves of engraved text (Anecdotes de l'ambassade de M. de Ferriol), and engraved leaf of music and 102 engraved handcoloured plates no'd 1-100 plus two unnumbered plates, supplementary folding plates, large paper copy in later red morocco, gilt fillets, gilt border, spine gilt in compartments, raised bands, g.e., later endpapers.
BL; GL; this edition not in Blackmer; Blackmer 591 for the first edition; Cohen de Ricci 392; Atabey 430 for this copy; this edition not in Colas.

The engravings were after drawings commissioned by French Ambassador Ferriol in Constantinople from French artist Van Mour. Along with the sixteenth century costume plates by Nicolay these formed the iconography of Ottoman costume and were copied over and over again and were enormously influential in forming the perceived image of the Turk and of the Turkish Empire at large for Europeans. Their importance was based on the fact that they were drawn from on the spot observation by Van Mour, an artist with entree to the Topkapi Palace granted by the Sultan to record life and ceremonial there.

139

ERNST II, Duke of Saxe-Coburg and Gotha.
Reise des Herzogs Ernst von Sachsen-Coburg-Gotha nach Aegypten und den Landern der Habab, Mensa und Bogos. Leipzig, Arnoldische Buchhandlung, 1864.

First edition. Large oblong folio, chromolithographed title, 19 chromolithographed plates by Robert Kretschmer, 4 mounted photographs on one leaf, two maps on one leaf, original wrappers preserved in later boards.
BL; Hilmy I, 349; Blackmer 554; not in Atabey.

First and apparently only edition of this account of a journey to Egypt, the Sudan and Eastern Abyssinia in 1862 by Ernest , Duke of Saxe-Coburg; he also used his wife's diary in preparing the text. They were accompanied on their expedition by the artist Robert Kretschmer, who lithographed his own drawings for the book and J.G. Banks. Kretschmer specialized in book illustration and was renowned for his watercolours. This series of plates are magnificent.

REISE

des Herzogs Ernst

von Sachsen-Coburg-Gotha,

nach

AEGYPTEN

und den Ländern der Habab

MENSA und BOGOS

mit 4 Photographien nach Handzeichnungen, 2 Charten u. 20 Zeichnungen nach der Natur aufgenomen u.chromolith. v. Robert Kretschmer

Farbendruck v. J G Bach, Leipzig

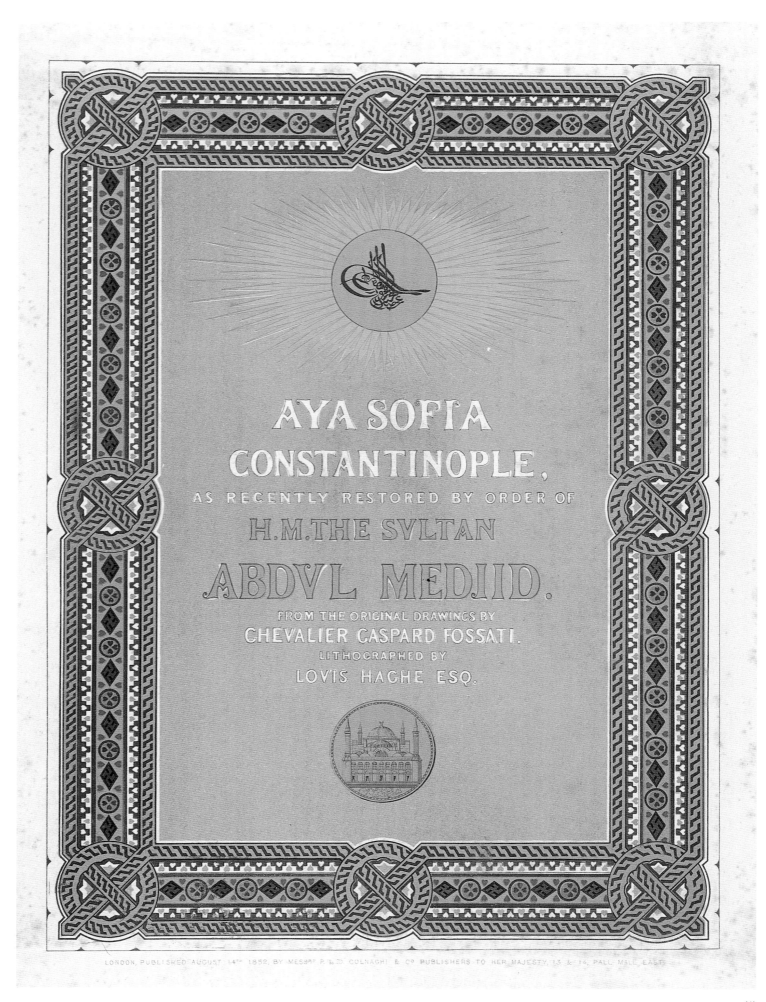

AYA SOFIA
CONSTANTINOPLE,
AS RECENTLY RESTORED BY ORDER OF
H.M.THE SVLTAN
ABDVL MEDJID.
FROM THE ORIGINAL DRAWINGS BY
CHEVALIER CASPARD FOSSATI.
LITHOGRAPHED BY
LOVIS HACHE ESQ.

LONDON, PUBLISHED AUGUST 14TH 1852, BY MESSRS P. & D. COLNAGHI & CO PUBLISHERS TO HER MAJESTY, 13 & 14, PALL MALL EAST.

LORD BYRON.

The Advocate and Supporter of the Greek Nation.   *La noble défenseur et Soutien de la Nation Grecque.*

FOSSATI, Gaspard.

Aya Sophia Constantinople, as recently restored by Order of H.M. The Sultan Abdul Medjid. From the original drawings by Chevalier Gaspard Fossati. Lithographed by Louis Hagche Esq.
London, Messrs. P. & D. Colnaghi & Co. Publishers to Her Majesty, 1852.

First edition. Large folio, 6pp., chromolithographed title by Owen Jones, and 25 handcoloured lithographed plates, all mounted on card, highlighted with gum Arabic, all captioned, preserved in contemporary morocco backed watered cloth folder, gilt ruled.
BL; Blackmer 619; Abbey 397. See C. Mango. Materials for the study of the mosaics of St. Sophia, 1962.

This edition with mounted plates, is the second state, of this first modern account of Aghia Sophia. The text is in French, in spite of the English title, and was edited by Adalbert de Beaumont from Fossati's notes. The chromolithographed title is almost certainly the work of Owen Jones. Fossati, an Italian was the court architect in Russia, and travelled to Constantinople in 1837 to do work on the Russian Embassy building there. On completion of that work, he was then employed by Sultan Abdul Medjid, charged with the restoration of the Aghia Sophia. He was commissioned to uncover mosaics, which were almost immediately recovered. He himself seems not to have made drawings of the mosaics, although a member of a German expedition to Constantinople at that time, did make some record. An enduring important work on a remarkable architectural achievement.

FRIEDEL, Adam de. [Les Grecs].
London and Paris, [1824 -] 1827.

Folio, no letterpress, 24 lithographed plates, on India paper mounted and finely handcoloured, contemporary russia, elaborately gilt panelled, surrounding the title, spine gilt in compartments, raised bands.
Not in Abbey or Atabey; Blackmer 633; Droulia 752-3, 1125-6.

Later edition (first edition 1824), issued without letterpress or title. The work went into numerous editions and contributing artists and consequently plates changed between first and second editions. There is some confusion as to Friedel's origins. He is supposed to be a Danish philhellene and was apparently passing himself off as a baron. St. Clair tells us that Friedel carried a lithographic press on his back through Greece, that he was at Missolonghi for a while with Byron and that he married the sister of John Hodges, one of Byron's artificers. A letter recommending Friedel to the notice of the London Greek Committee is known. In any event Friedel seems to have been in Greece from about 1821 to mid-1824. He settled in England and his first lithograph appears dated September, 1824.

GELL, Sir William.

The Topography of Troy, And Its Vicinity; Illustrated And Explained By Drawings And Descriptions. Dedicated, By Permission, To Her Grace The Duchess Of Devonshire.
London, By C. Whittingham for T.N. Longman and O. Rees, 1804.

First and only edition. Small folio, 30 handcoloured aquatints no'ed 1-45 together with the vignettes in the letterpress, contemporary russia, label gilt lettered, edges red.
BL; GL; Weber, 1; Abbey 399; Lascarides 81; Brunet II, 1519 also cites a second edition, 1807; but this is not confirmed.

Gell visited the Troad in December 1801 in company with Dodwell. He used the Camera Lucida to produce very accurate sketches. Gell fixed the site of Troy at Bounarbashi, in agreement with Le Chevalier's theories. "Certainly the most beautiful book on Troy ever published" – Lascarides.

GOUPIL FESQUET, Frederic A.A.

Voyage d'Horace Vernet en Orient.
Paris, Challamel, [1843].

First edition, first issue. Large 8vo, [ii] 328pp., list of plates, 16 handcoloured lithographed plates, original straight grained cloth, ornately decorated to a Romantic style in gilt and blind, spine flat and similarly decorated, g.e.
Blackmer 718; Weber 309; Carteret III, p. 594; Lipperheide 1597; Atabey 511.
Colas 1275; Lipperheide 1597.

Goupil Fesquet travelled in the Levant from October 1839 to February 1840, in company with Horace Vernet. He later produced many manuals on drawing, painting and craftwork. When in Constantinople Goupil made daguerrotypes of the Saint Sophia in a snowstorm which he developed in his hotel bedroom. Sadly none of these survive, except as engraved copies.

31

PLATE XII.

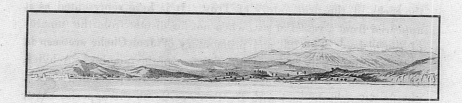

This small sketch comprises a part of the coast, about a mile in extent, from the tumulus of Achilles on the right, to the castle of Koum Kale on the left. Mount Ida is seen over the tumulus of Achilles, nearly in the same direction, as in the preceding Plate. The summit of the tumulus of Patroclus is also distinguishable; and between the high poplars and the village of Koum Kale some rocks are discoverable, which seem more positively to determine the original shore. The village stands on a long point of sand terminated by the fortress, which is often named the Castle of the Sand, in allusion to its situation. The mountain, seen over the village, is that which divides the vale of Thymbra from the Hellespont, and is a continuation of an extensive chain, reaching from Gargarus to the sea, and forming the northern and eastern boundary of the plain of Troy. Beyond the point of the castle the shores again recede, and a shallow bay affords an anchorage to the small vessels of the country.

HARDINGE, Hon. Charles Stewart.

Second Viscount Hardinge. Sketches of Sebastopol. London, Henry Graves & Co., 1855.

First edition. Oblong folio, vignette title tinted lithograph, and 10 handcoloured lithographed plates, folding map, original red morocco backed cloth gilt ruled, lettered direct on upper cover. Not in Abbey, Tooley, Colas, Atabey, Blackmer.

Hardinge a talented amateur artist in watercolours would seem to have been in the Crimea either as an observer or for political reasons. As the result of a serious childhood accident he was unable to join the army as expected and was known for his career in India as private secretary to his father Viscount Hardinge. He is best known as an illustrator for a lithographed set of plates of India (see elsewhere in this catalogue), but this is also an attractive and informative series of plates. From 1868 he was a Trustee of the National Portrait Gallery and in 1876 chairman of the trustees, an office which he actively filled till his death. Owing to his father's friendship with Sir Edwin Henry Landseer he was brought up among artistic associations.

HOBHOUSE, J.C.

A Journey through Albania and other Provinces of Turkey, in Europe and Asia to Constantinople, during the Years 1809 and 1810.
London, James Cawthorn... and sold by Sharpe and Hailes... Bell and Bradfute, Edinburgh and N. Mahon, Dublin, 1813.

First edition. Large 4to, pp. xix, [1], 1152, one leaf text, one leaf errata, 2 leaves engraved music, frontispiece, 2 folding maps, and 1 plan and 17 handcoloured aquatinted plates, contemporary Russia, double gilt fillet, blindstamped border spines raised bands, gilt in compartments, m.e.
Abbey Travel 202; Atabey 584; BL; This edition not in Weber; Blackmer 821. This edition not in Abbey but see 202. See P. Graham, Byron's Bulldog. Letters of J.C. Hobhouse to Lord Byron, 1984, and M. Joyce, My Friend H., 1948. Also Leslie Marchand, Byron's Letters and Journals, Vol. II.

There is another issue in two vols., 4to. The second edition also appeared in 1813. A much published work, among others a new edition appeared in 1855, under the name of Baron Broughton, Hobhouse was Lord Broughton. Hobhouse was a close friend of Byron and accompanied him on his first journey to Greece. This work is of great interest not only for the light it sheds on that journey, but for the mass of information Hobhouse provides, in particular on the court and character of Ali Pashaat Joannina. Hobhouse maintained his friendship with Byron through all the troubled years of the poet's life, and in 1823 when he joined the London Greek Committee, he may have played some part in Byron's decision to go to Greece. Some of the interesting plates are of the Athenian monuments in this work and were commissioned by Byron from the artist Jacob Lynckh, later involved in the excavations of Aegina with the architect Charles Cockerell, who also produced drawings for Hobhouse's work.

LIBAY, Karl Ludwig [and] Kremer, Alfred von.
Egypte, Scenes de Voyage en Orient, (Aegypten Reisebilder aus dem Orient Reisebilder aus dem Orient). Vienna, L. Libay, 1857-[60].

First and only edition, 5 original parts, folio, map, letterpress, 60 handcoloured lithographed plates after the author on card and loose as issued in original boards converted to folder, letterpress title in German and French trimmed and laid down on front upper cover, preserved in modern half red morocco linen backed box, spine gilt.
Blackmer 1016; BL; Brunet III, 697; Hilmy I, 385; ONL.

The descriptive text is by Orientalist Alfred von Kremer. The work was dedicated to Count Joseph von Bruenner, Libay's travelling companion and son of his patron Count August Ferdinand Bruenner, famous for the building of Grafenneg Castle in Lower Austria. He had financed this expedition to Egypt. It was on this journey that Libay produced the illustrations for this work. Libay was a Slovakian/Hungarian artist who had based himself in Vienna. In this work he applied the principles of landscape painting to Orientalist subjects with some success (Hitzel)

MAYER, Luigi. Ansichten von Palestina.
Leipzig, Baumgaertnersche Buchhandlung, n.d. [but 1810].

3 vols., oblong folio, 36 handcoloured aquatint plates, together with German translation described below, contemporary wrappers, preserved in linen box.
This edition not in Abbey Travel.

This German translation was edited by Rosenmueller (see his own work below). At the same time he produced Mayer's Views of Turkey etc., translated into German and published in Leipzig, dated 1812, as Ansichten von der Tuerkei Hauptsachlich von Caramanien, einem bisher wenig bekannten Theile von Kleinasien, a selection edited by Rosenmueller, and offered together. These two parts were also offered together as here in the French edition of the works.

MAYER, Luigi.
Views in Palestine and other Parts of the Ottoman Empire. London, 1804 [and] 1803.

2 vols. in one, folio, title in French and English, 48 handcoloured aquatint plates, 20th century three quarters calf, spine raised bands gilt, label gilt over marbled boards.
Abbey Travel 369.

The volumes are split into Vol. I Views in Egypt and Vol. II Views in the Ottoman Empire. These are often uniformly bound with Views in Egypt.

150

MAYER, Luigi [and] WATTS, William.
Views in Turkey in Europe and Asia, comprising Romelia, Bulgaria, Wallachia…
London, William Watts, 1801.

First edition. Folio, 60 handcoloured aquatint plates, 3 engraved titles, later 19th century red morocco backed cloth, spine gilt ruled in compartments.
Abbey Travel 371.

This was the set of plates being worked by William Watts after Mayer. (See description below of Views in the Ottoman Dominions which appeared in advance of this work.)

151

MAYER, Luigi.
Views in the Ottoman Dominions, in Europe in Asia, and some of the Mediterranean Islands, from the Original Drawings taken for Sir Robert Ainslie, by Luigi Mayer, F.A.S. with descriptions historical and illustrative.…
London, T. Bensley, 1810.

First collected edition. 2 vols., large folio, preliminaries include a list of plates and 70 pp., explanations of the plates, 71 handcoloured aquatint plates, original boards, paper labels on spine, modern linen covered box.
Abbey Travel 371; Tooley 321.

Forty-six of these plates first appeared in William Watts' Views of Turkey in Europe and Asia, 1801. This work was being prepared at the same time as Mayer's Egypt and was the first to contain engravings of Mayer's drawings of Turkey. It is curious that two engravers were preparing plates of Mayer's drawings simultaneously. Watts' work was in preparation until 1806, the period during which plates for Mayer's Egypt, Palestine and Caramania were being engraved by Thomas Milton for Robert Bowyer. The new plates in Mayer's Ottoman Dominions depict views of Sicily, Gozo and the Lipari islands, as well as ancient sites in Samos and Ephesus. Again these were places which Mayer had visited on his tour of 1792 and perhaps even earlier. Mayer had studied with Piranesi and was employed by the King of Sicily. He then took service with Ainslie in Constantinople.

152

MAYER, Luigi.
Views in Egypt, from the original Drawings in the Possession of Sir Robert Ainslie, taken during his Embassy to Constantinople.
London, Thomas Bensley… for R. Bowyer, 1801.

First edition. Large folio, iii, 102 [2], i, [1-2], 48 handcoloured aquatinted plates, large paper copy, contemporary red straight grained red morocco, elaborate double gilt border enclosing central lozenge gilt, g.e.
Colas 2018; Abbey Travel 369; Blackmer 1097.

Mayer was hired to accompany a young Englishman on a tour of the Levant in 1792. It is possible that Ainslie's decision to reproduce the drawings was due to the interest aroused by Napoleon's Egyptian campaign, although the plates in fact show pre-Napoleonic Egypt.

To
Sir ROBERT AINSLIE
this Collection of VIEWS
in the
TURKISH PROVINCES
taken during his Embassy
to
CONSTANTINOPLE
is gratefully inscribed
by his much obliged &
obed.^{nt}   Servant
W^m   WATTS

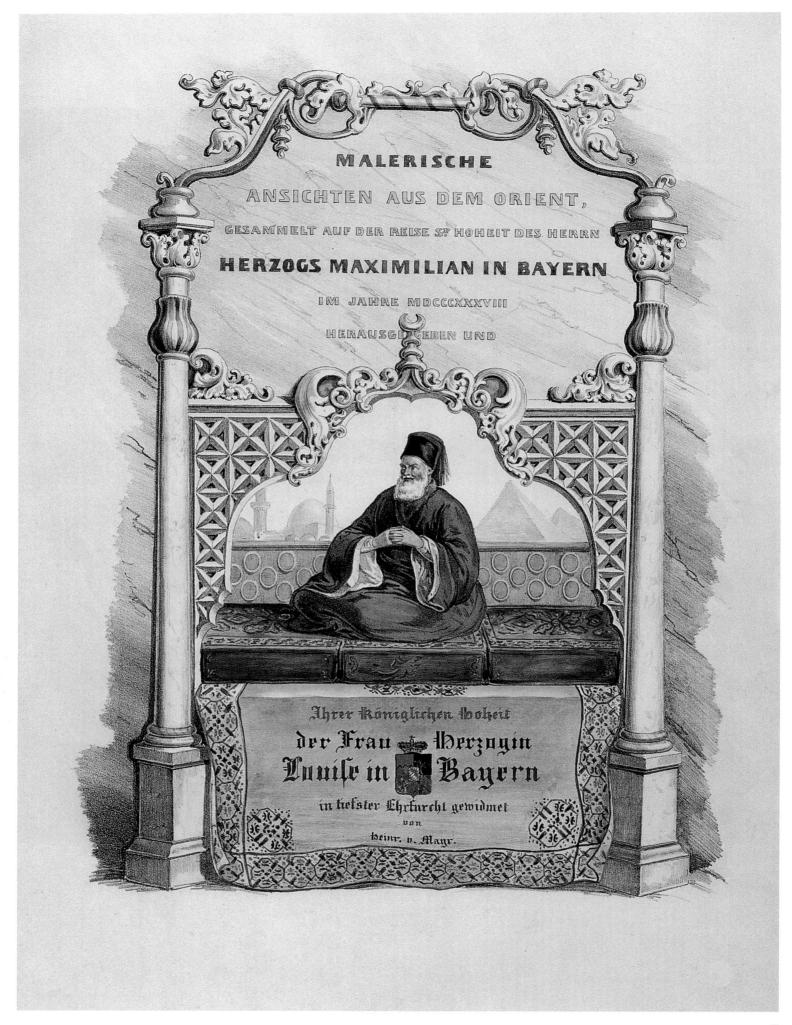

MAYR, Heinrich von and FISCHER, Sebastien.
Malerische Ansichten aus dem Orient, gesammelt auf der Reise… Herzogs Maximilian v. Bayern nach Nubien, Aegypten, Palaestina…im Jahre 1838 und herausgegeben von Heinrich von Mayr.
Munich, [1839].

First edition. Folio, 60 handcoloured lithographed plates on light card within gilt lithographed decorative border, in original boards, upper cover elaborately blindstamped, preserved in 20th century morocco backed cloth covered box.
Not in GL; Tobler p. 161; not in NUC; nor in BNC; Rohricht 1871; Ibrahim-Hilmy II, pg. 26; Lipperheide Ma22.

This was the account of Duke Maximilian von Bayern's journey through Nubia, Egypt, Palestine in 1838. The plates are scenes of Eastern life, including a doctor's visit to the Harem. Interestingly because of his professional status he was the only detailed external source of information re women's lives, health etc. in the Harem at the time, a source of great interest to European observers. Mayr has also included detailed plates of furniture, clothing, musical instruments and decorative tiles. The costume plates include that of a Greek woman at her embroidery. A magnificently produced work.

MONTAUT, Henry de.
L'Egypte Moderne. Paris, Henri Plon, 1869.

Large oblong folio, woodcut illustrations, 10 chromolithographed plates framed in gilt with Arabic titling in red at base of each plate "Henri Plon/chrom. De Bequet", mounted on card, and loose as issued in original red cloth ruled in blind, gilt lettering with arms of the Khedive, gilt crescents in each corner.
Hilmy pg. 171.

Attractive Egyptian genre scenes from approximately the same period as Preziosi was active also with scenes of life in Constantinople.

NEALE, Frederick Adam.
Travels through some Parts of Germany, Poland, Moldavia, and Turkey.
London, Longman, Hurst, Rees, Orme and Brown; Edinburgh, A. Constable, 1818.

4to, title, directions for plates, 1 leaf verso with errata, contents, text pp.1-295, page 296 blank, advertisements, 11 handcoloured aquatint plates, four plates with two views to a plate, signed A.N. del and I. Clark sc., contemporary half morocco over cloth gilt.
Abbey Travel 19; Tooley (1954) 344; Cat. Russica, No. N261.

Plates include a view of the English Ambassador's Palace at Therapia on the Bosphorus, a Turkish boatman and two views on the Black Sea. A French and German edition were published.

PIEROTTI, Dr Ermete.
Le Cantique des Cantiques. Illustre et Commente sur le Sol Meme de la Palestine.
Paris, J. Cherbuliez; Monrocq, J.U., 1871.

First edition. 4to, 12 handcoloured lithographed plates of costumes of the Holy Land, original red cloth backed printed boards lettered in red, original upper wrapper bound in.
Colas 2360.

Scarce. Pierotti worked as an engineer for the Pasha of Jerusalem during the 1830s.

PILLEAU, Henry.
Sketches in Egypt. London, Dickinson & Son, 1845.

First edition. Large folio, subscribers, dedication, preface, description of plates, 12 tinted lithographed plates handcoloured, later half green morocco by Sangorski and Sutcliffe.
Abbey Travel 271 (coloured copy); Ibrahim-Hilmy Vol. II, 119; Gay 2497; Blackmer 1313; Atabey 956.

Apparently first and only edition. Coloured copies of this work are also known, as here. Pilleau travelled in Egypt in company with Lt. Col. George Everest, former surveyor-general of India. The list of subscribers is made up mostly of medical and militiamen, and includes James Lister. The plates illustrate ancient Egyptian temples and monuments.

158

PRISSE D'AVENNES, Achille Constant Theodore Emile.

Oriental Album. Characters, Costumes, and Modes of Life in the Valley of the Nile. Illustrated from designs taken on the spot by E. Prisse. With descriptive letter-press by James Augustus St. John...
London, James Madden, 1848.

First edition. Large folio, portrait frontispiece, text, 30 handcoloured lithographed plates, numbered by hand on mounts and on decorative chromolithographed title, lithographed by Lemercier, Devaria and others, mounted and loose as issued in half green morocco backed portfolio, morocco title piece on upper cover, this converted into folder.
BL; Blackmer 1357; Carre I, pp. 297-319; not in Abbey; Atabey 101.

A second edition appeared of which there is also a copy in this collection in its original printed wrappers, published in 1851. In the Atabey copy with plates on card, the text was issued separately. Prisse D'Avennes spent many years in Egypt after 1826, first as an engineer in the service of Mehmet Ali. After 1836 he explored Egypt disguised as an Arab and using the name Edris Effendi; during this period he worked as an archaeologist in the Nile Valley. From 1839 to 1843 he excavated at Thebes with George Lloyd, to whom the work is dedicated and whose portrait serves as a frontispiece. It was due to Lloyd that Prisse embarked on the series of drawings which make up this work. St. John, who wrote the text, had travelled in Egypt and Nubia, mainly on foot in 1832-33.

(An 1850 folio edition of the same work, Oriental Album. Characters, Costumes and Modes of Life, in the Valley of the Nile, preserved in modern cloth covered box also in this collection.)

159
REID, John.

Turkey and the Turks; being the Present State of the Ottoman Empire.
London, Robert Tyas, 1840.

8vo, lithographed frontispiece and five lithographed plates, four handcoloured, two maps, original decorated cloth.
Not in Abbey, Colas or Lipperheide.

The author travelled to Turkey to take up a position as physician to the British Embassy in Constantinople. This is a description of the overland journey from Jassy in Moldavia to the Danube and then via the Black Sea to Constantinople.

158

160

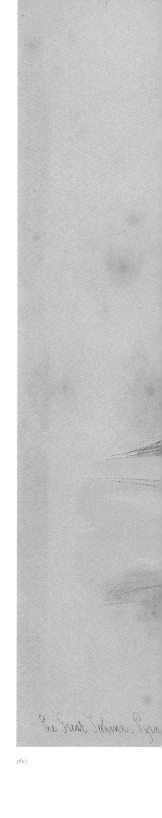

160

160

ROBERTS, David.

The Holy Land, Syria, Idumea, Arabia, Egypt and Nubia From Drawings made on the Spot... with historical Descriptions by the Rev. George Croly [and] William Brockendon.

London, F.G. Moon, 1842-49.

First edition, this is one of a limited number of de luxe subscribers' copies. 6 vols., large folio, 6 handcoloured lithographed titles with pictorial vignettes and 241 lithographed plates, with titles and plates finely coloured by hand, on India proof paper and mounted on card, uncoloured

lithographed portrait of Roberts by C. Baugnier, engraved maps, drawn on stone by Louis Haghe after David Roberts, the complete set uniformly bound in mid 19th century red morocco, elaborate gilt borders, spines gilt, raised bands, inner gilt dentelles, g.e. Abbey Travel 385 & 272; Tooley (1954) 401; Blackmer 1432; Gay 25; Ibrahim-Hilmy II, p. 176; Lipperheide No. 1590; Rohricht 1984; Tobler, p. 229, BL, this edition not in GL.

A complete set of the subscribers edition with handcoloured plates mounted on card. David Roberts

enjoyed wide popularity in his day. His outstanding success was certainly this complete publication, and it is on this that the modern appreciation of his work is based. The powerful images of Baalbec, Petra, Egypt and the Holy Land fully demonstrate the artist's skilful draughtsmanship and use of dramatic perspective to portray the majesty of what he sees. Robert's early training as a set designer for the theatre is perhaps nowhere so clearly evident. At the time of publication, such dramatic representations of the East had rarely been encountered in the West. Consequently, Robert's

work captivated the public imagination and set the archetypal standard so often imitated by later artists.

However, it is not only Roberts's draughtsmanship that sets this work apart from so many others. It is also, as is so often noted, the quality of Day and Haghe's lithography, considered by Abbey to be "the apotheosis of 19th-century publishing and the apotheosis of the tinted lithograph". This is particularly true of the desert plates, where the lithographer seems to have magically captured the shimmering effect of the heat and the sand.

160

160

ROSENMUELLER, Ernst Friedrich Karl.
Biblische Geographie.
Leipzig, Baumgaertner, 1823-30.

8 vols., 8vo, original wrappers preserved in modern cloth covered box, spine gilt labelled.
Rohricht 1667.

Rosenmueller was one of the editors and publishers of the German edition of Luigi Mayer's illustrated works on Palestine and the Ottoman Dominions, which he published as a set (see above). This is Rosenmueller's bibliography of early books on Palestine I-III.

SIMPSON, William.
The Seat of War in the East, 1855-56.
London, Paul and Domenic Colnaghi & Co., Day & Son, Paris, Goupil, Leipzig, Otto Weigel, 1855-56.

First and second series bound in one vol., folio, coloured vignette titles, lithographed dedication, verso with list of plates, Vol. II, 1 leaf, text pp. 1-14 in double columns, 79 handcoloured lithographed plates heightened with gum, mounted on card, Arabic and interleaved with all 36 outline key engravings all by and after William Simpson, contemporary half red morocco, gilt ruled over original red cloth, upper cover gilt lettered, spine with raised bands gilt ruled, g.e., preserved in modern dark blue linen box.
Abbey Travel 237.

There were two issues at least of the First Series Volume. The first issue had the keys and text supplied separately in a small 4to volume with the title Descriptive Sketches, illustrating Mr. William Simpson's Drawings of the Seat of War in the East. First Series. By George Brackenbury. 1855. In this volume there are ten keys. In the second issue, which may well represent the form in which the First Series appeared when put on sale with the Second, as a complete work, twelve pages of text are bound in, and the keys face their appropriate plates. The publishers' Notice mentioned above as appearing at the end of some copies of the First Series, clearly refers to the separate text published for the first issue. As a publisher's announcement in December 1854 shows, Simpson had been commissioned to proceed to Sebastopol immediately, by Colnaghi's. This was the beginning of the enterprise which earned him the name "Crimean Simpson". These plates are indeed an impressive piece of work, not only artistically and technically, but also as pictorial reporting. It is still regarded as a brilliant example of lithographic work. Simpson must in this way rank as an early war correspondent, although not so influential with the pencil as was William Howard Russell with the pen. Simpson had

become associated with Day, the lithographic printer of this book, at about the time Louis Haghe, Day's partner earlier, gave up lithography to concentrate on water-colour painting. This was in 1852. The C. Haghe who lithographed some of these plates was Charles, Louis Haghe's younger brother, who had constantly helped Louis in his lithographic work. In 1835 Simpson entered an architect's office in Glasgow, and there his taste for art was developed, and two years afterwards he was apprenticed to the firm of Allan & Ferguson, lithographers, Glasgow. There he was given the task of sketching many old buildings for Stuart's Views of Glasgow, which was published in 1848 by the firm. Simpson removed to London in 1851, and was employed by Day & Son, then the leading lithographers. After the Crimean War broke out Simpson was engaged on views of the Baltic battles for Colnaghi & Son; and when that firm decided to publish a large illustrated work on the Crimean campaign from sketches made on the spot, Simpson was selected for the work on Day's recommendation. He started on short notice, arrived at Balaclava in November 1854, and remained with the British army till the fall of Sebastopol. Simpson was thus the pioneer war-artist, and received several commissions to paint incidents in the war for the Queen.

SPILSBURY, Francis B.
Picturesque Scenery in the Holy Land and Syria, delineated during the Campaigns of 1799 and 1800.
London, Edward Orme, 1803.

First edition. Small folio with good large margins, 19 handcoloured aquatint plates, plus mezzotint frontispiece portrait by Bell after Chandler of Sir William Sidney Smith, contemporary red morocco, over contemporary marbled boards, spine gilt ruled, gilt titling piece surrounded by Greek key design.
BL; GL; not in Weber; Abbey Travel 381; Tooley 464; Atabey for third edition of 1823; Blackmer 1585.

The work was published in five parts. Spilsbury was the surgeon on board H.M.S. Tigre, commanded by Sydney Smith, the hero of Acre, to whom the work is dedicated. The Tigre took part in the English campaigns against the French in Egypt and Syria. Spilsbury's plates include views in Syria and Palestine and genre scenes, several of which depict officers of the expedition.

STACKELBERG, Baron Otto Magnus von.
Costumes et Usages des Peuples de la Grece Moderne, graves d'apres les Dessins executes dans les lieux en 1811. Rome, 1825.

First edition. Small folio, 40 handcoloured aquatint plates, nineteenth century scarlet cloth, gilt and blindstamped, rebacked in matching straight-grained morocco.
Blackmer 1591 for the German edition with same collation plus frontispiece; Colas and Lipperheide cite lithographed editions.

This appears to be the first edition of a work later lithographed. An Italian edition of Naples 1827 appears to have been one of the piracies which Stackelberg complained of in his introduction to the German edition, also with engraved plates, the only difference being that in the Rome edition Stackelberg's name appears in the imprint. It was these piracies which persuaded him to produce the German edition. The plates of costumes constitute Stackelberg's first published work on Greece, where he travelled from 1810-14. He was in Athens with Byron and travelled and worked with Cockerell, Haller von Hallerstein, Gropius, Linckh (see Hobhouse) and Foster in excavating various archaeological sites, particularly Bassae. He is probably best known for La Grece, Vues Pittoresques et Topographiques.

TANCOIGNE, J.M.
Voyage a Smyrne, dans l'Archipel et l'Ile de Candie, en 1811, 1812, 1813 & 1814.
Paris, Nepveu, 1817.

First edition. 2 vols. in one, 12mo, 2 long handcoloured folding panoramic plates of processions of the Sultans during two Bayrams, after Antoine Ignace Melling, contemporary tree calf, spine flat, gilt border, g.e.
Blackmer 1628; BL; GL; Weber 50; Malakis pp. 76-8.

Tancoigne was attached to the French Embassy in Persia and made three trips to Constantinople. He states in his preface to this work that he is not interested in antiquity but in the present day state of the countries he visited. He was particularly interested in the customs and character of the Greeks. Malakis remarks that the work was very critical.

TCHERNETSOV [CHERNETSOV].
Grigorii Grigor'evich and Nikanor Grigor'evich (1805–79). Palestine. Views [in Russian and Hebrew], drawn from nature by Academicians G. and N. Chernetsov, in the years 1842 and 1843 (accompanying text in French). n.p.; n.d. [although censorship granted for part 1 in 1844; part 2 not given; part 3, 1845; part 4, 1845.

4 parts in one vol., Part I, folio, lithographed handcoloured title, one leaf of text, and 6 coloured lithographed plates; Part II, title, one leaf of text, and plates 7-13 plates, all lithographed and coloured; Part III, title, one leaf of text, coloured lithographed plates 14-19; Part IV, title, one leaf of text, coloured lithographed plates 20-25. N. Obol'ianov, Catalogue of Russian Illustrated Books 1725-1860, Moscow, 1915. For biography of artist G. Smirnov, Chernetsovy, Moscow & Leningrad, 1949.

Some of the plates included are as follows: View of Jerusalem from the Damascus Road; View of Ramla; Fort of David; Valley of the Jordan; Solomon's Ponds; Building on Sion; Hill of Eleon; Place of the Samaritan's Kindness.

VAN LENNEP, Rev. Henry.
The Oriental Album. Twenty Illustrations, in Oil Colors of the People and Scenery of Turkey, with an explanatory and descriptive text…
New York, Anson D.F. Randolph, 1862.

First and apparently only edition. Folio, pp. 48 colour printed lithographs, lithographed title and 20 coloured lithographed plates, original decorated cloth, vignette on upper cover of a woman seated on a camel, shaded by a palm tree, a crescent and star in the sky.
GL; not in BLC; Blackmer 1715; not in Colas; Atabey 1274.

Van Lennep worked as a missionary among the Armenians from 1840 to 1861, for much of that time in Tokat, the home of many rich Armenians, and his work is particularly interesting for illustrations of Armenian life and costume in the Ottoman Empire.

167

Mrs Moore Wife of the British Consul at Beyrout in an Arab Dress.

VELDE, Charles William Meredith van de.
Le Pays d'Israel Collections de Cent Vues Prises d'apres Nature dans La Syrie et La Palestine....
Paris, Jules Renouard, 1857.

First edition. Large folio, 100 lithographed plates, (no.74 forms lithographed title), approximately half of the plates chromolithographed, several of these heightened by hand, contemporary green morocco backed cloth, raised bands ruled in gilt and blind.
Blackmer 1722; BL; GL; not in Abbey; Tobler p. 184.

Apparently 300 copies of the work were printed. A certain number were proof copies. The lithographer's stones were destroyed. The proof copies taken from a copy at one time in the possession of B. Quaritch Ltd. Are much taller than ordinary copies, and the plates are printed on card and include a plan of Jerusalem. Van de Velde had published an account of his journey in German and Dutch.

WERNER, Carl.
Nilbilder auf seine Reise durch Aegypten nach der Natur aufgenommen.
Hamburg, Dorling, [1871-75].

First edition. Folio, 24 chromolithographed plates by G.W. Seitz, these mounted on card, in original red ornately gilt cloth, vignette gilt of sphinx in centre of upper cover, morocco backed, preserved in modern morocco and cloth box.
Blackmer 1947; Hilmy II, 324.

Blackmer makes no mention of this German edition. The English edition of 1871-75 seems to have been the first. It is possible that there was a de luxe format without the letterpress, the plates mounted on card. This was a common form of deluxe edition and several notable works appeared thus, e.g.Robert's Holy Land, Dodwell etc.

Werner was a Professor at the Academy of Leipzig. He travelled in the Levant in 1862-4 and c. 1870. His first excursion was productive of Jerusalem, Bethlehem and the Holy Places, 1865, with text and this journey into Egypt was a part of his second journey. The plates are dated on the surfaces from 1870 to 1874, but it seems unlikely that he remained in Egypt for so long. These dates may refer to paintings done in his studio from sketches, or else he may have travelled in Egypt during five consecutive winters. In 1882 Werner planned a similar publication on Athens, wanting Schliemann to write the introductory text but the work seems not to have appeared, although Blackmer states that two plates for this work have been seen. As well as street scenes in Cairo, there are views of the Nile and the Temple at Philae among others in this work.

WHARNCLIFFE, Lord [STUART-WORTLEY, John].
Sketches in Egypt and in the Holy Land.
London, by Colnaghi, [c.1855].

Large folio, lithographed title with handcoloured vignette, 17 tinted lithographed plates, handcoloured, morocco backed cloth, upper cover gilt lettered direct, spine gilt lettered. BL.

It is interesting that Lord Wharncliffe, then a politician in opposition, found time to edit the letters and works of his ancestress, Lady Mary Wortley-Montagu. His edition appeared in 5 vols in 1837, and superceded that of Dallaway. It was reissued in 1861 and 1893. This work by Wharncliffe appears to be relatively scarce.

WILKIE, SIR David.
Sir David Wilkie's Sketches in Turkey, Syria and Egypt, 1840 & 1841. Drawn on Stone by David Nash.
[London, Graves and Warmsley, Printed by C. Hullmandel, 1843].

First edition. Large Folio, 2pp. manuscript text in blue ink, 25 handcoloured lithographed plates and title, drawn on stone by David Nash and printed by C. Hullmandel, all mounted on card and loose in contemporary morocco backed folder of watered cloth, red morocco label, preserved in 20th century morocco backed linen box.
BL; GL; Weber 1144; Abbey Travel 379; Hilmy II, 329; Blackmer 1796; Atabey 1334.

Wilkie set out for the East in 1840 to gather material for a series of biblical illustrations. He visited Constantinople, Beirut, Jerusalem, Cairo, and Alexandria, where he painted a portrait of Mehmet Ali now in the Tate Gallery, London. He died on the return journey in 1846, and his large collection of sketches was sold to various collectors. Earlier he had been appointed Painter to the King for Scotland by King George IV and on his travels he had met up with French Orientalist, Delacroix (Hitzel).

WILLYAMS, Rev. Cooper.
A Voyage up the Mediterranean in His Majesty's Ship the Swiftsure...
London, for John Hearne, 1802.

First edition. Folio, 43 handcoloured aquatint plates, on large paper, contemporary straightgrained morocco gilt, elaborate double borders, spine gilt in compartments, raised bands, lettered direct, g.e., bookplate of Samuel George Smith.
Abbey Travel 196.

See footnote below.

WILLYAMS, Rev. Cooper.
A Selection of Views in Egypt, Palestine, Rhodes, Italy, Minorca and Gibraltar.
London, John Hearne, 1822.

Second edition, second issue. Small folio, 36 no'ed handcoloured aquatint plates, later 19th century half morocco over marbled boards, spine raised bands, gilt ruled.
BL; Weber 114; Abbey Travel 198; Gay 28; Lipperheide 570; Ibrahim-Hilmy Vol. II, p. 335; Atabey 1339; Blackmer 1814.

This second edition was published posthumously. The work first appeared in 1802, see above, as a Voyage up the Mediterranean, with 43 plates. This edition includes plates 3-11, 16, and 22-43 from the original edition, re-aquatinted and in places re-etched. Four new unsigned plates were added to this second edition. Willyams was Chaplain on H.M.S. Swiftsure during the Egyptian campaign against the French and was present at the Battle of the Nile. The first edition plates are after his own drawings.

WITTMAN, William.
Travels in Turkey, Asia-Minor, Syria and across the Desert into Egypt during the Years 1799, 1800, and 1801.
London, for Richard Phillips by T. Gillet... 1803.

4to, large folding frontispiece, large folding handcoloured map, large folding plate of firman, and 21 plates of which 15 costume plates, these handcoloured, 5 uncoloured engravings, two folding, handcoloured map, contemporary tree calf, spine flat and gilt ruled, label gilt on spine.
BL; Weber 647; Blackmer 1832; not in Abbey or Colas but Lipperheide for German edition.

Wittman was a member of the Anglo-Turkish expeditionary force which travelled overland from Constantinople to Egypt in 1799 to take part in the campaign against the French. Two of the plates nos. 8, Jaffa, and 19, Fort Julian, are after drawings by Spilsbury and several of the unsigned costume plates were used by McLean for his Military Costume of Turkey.

YOUNG, John.
A Series of Portraits of the Emperors of Turkey from the Foundation of the Monarchy to the Year 1815. Engraved from pictures painted at Constantinople. Commenced under the auspices of Sultan Selim the Third, and completed by command of Sultan Mahmoud the Second. With a biographical account of each of the Emperors.
London, William Bulmer and Co., 1815.

First edition, second issue. Folio, 30 mezzotint plates, printed in colours and with additional handcolouring, magnificent imprints, contemporary half morocco, spine ornately gilt, g.e., original blue endpapers.
BL; not in GL; Abbey Travel 372; Blackmer 1863 (for first issue); Lipperheide 1429; Tooley 516; Atabey 1350.

From collection of Jay Gould (1836-1892); Lyndhurst bookplate. With reference to Mahmoud II, no imprint and accompanied by French version, English title as subtitle with no imprint, no captioning. It is possible that this second issue refers to the time when Young took over the work himself. He had begun work on these portraits in about 1803. Work stopped in 1807 when the reforms of Selim III led to the insurrection of the Janissaries; Selim was murdered and Mahmoud II came to the throne. In 1810 Young himself was given permission to publish the work by Mahmoud, and he continued with the engraving himself. This second issue title has Mahmouds's name as well as Selim's on the title. The engravings are after the original portraits by a Greek artist in Constantinople. Young was the official engraver in mezzotint to the Prince Regent, the future George IV.

YOUNG, Lieut. C.R.
Overland Sketches.
London, Dickinson & Son, [c. 1845].

First and only edition. Small folio, lithographed title, 14 handcoloured lithographed plates on 11, nos. 1-2, 7-8, 13-14 on three sheets, lithographed title with title vignette, original printed boards.
Blackmer 1860; not in GL; Abbey; NUC; Hilmy; BLC;.Atabey.

An apparently scarce work. Nothing is known of Young. Blackmer states that Aden was annexed to British India in 1839 and that this work was probably published soon after this. Plates include a lithographed title with vignette of Aden; views of Cairo; the Great Pyramid and the Sphynx; two of Thebes or surround; the Gateway to Karnak; First Cataract (Philae); the beginnings of the Desert and a Mirage.

SULTAN AMURAT KHAN IV.ᵐᵉ   DIX SEPTIEME EMPEREUR OTHOMAN

Imperial Russia

177

ACKERMANN, Rudolph.
Historical Sketch of Moscow.
London, Ackermann, Repository of the Arts, 1813.

Folio. First edition. Title, introduction, text pp. 1-27, 4to, 12 handcoloured aquatint plates, original printed boards, rebacked in red morocco, publisher's printed label on upper cover.
Abbey Travel 224; Cat. Russica, No. S1456; Martin Hardie, pp. 104, 310; Prideaux pp. 227, 340, 374; Tooley (1954), No. 262.

Plates unsigned, view of the Entrance into Moscow; general views of Moscow; a view of the Imperial Palace of the Kremlin at Moscow, the Wall of the Kremlin; view of the Old Wooden Theatre at Moscow.

178

[ALBRECHT, Prinz von Preussen, (Friedrich-Heinrich)].
Im Kaukasus, 1862.
Berlin, A.W. Hayn, 1862.

2 vols, small 4to text and oblong folio atlas of plates, text chromolithographed title, vi pp., preface, 1ff. index, 603pp., text decorated with three vignettes, 1 unnumbered ff. a lithographed map, 31 unnumbered chromolithographed plates, including two maps; folio atlas vol., original wrapper serving as title, 11 unnumbered chromolithographed plates, in original white parchment, Russian Imperial eagles gilt on sides of each vol.
Not in Abbey: Colas 53; Lipperheide 1386; not in Miansarov.

The plates represent in greater part Caucasian costume after T. Horschelt and H. Kretzschmer, many of a military nature and showing army life in the wild. A highly attractive and apparently scarce work. Kretschmer was a German artist of some note and a costumier at the Hoftheater in Berlin.

ALEXANDER, William.
The Costume of the Russian Empire.
London, Miller, 1803.

Large 4to, descriptions in English and French, 73 handcoloured stipple engraved plates, by J. Dudley for William Miller, half red morocco.
Abbey Travel 244; Cat. Russ. C1187; Colas No. 702; Lipperheide 134; Martin Hardie pg. 151; Prideaux pg. 317.

Plates include costumes of Esthonia, Tcheremhisia, Votiakia, Ostiak, Tartar, Boukhara, Barabinzia, Kirghi, Samoyed, Kmatshatka, Mongolia. The fourth in the series of costume books issued by William Miller. The plates in this work are closely copied, but somewhat enlarged, from a book by J.G. Georgi, published by Carl Wilhelm Muller at St. Petersburg, 4 vols., 4to, 1776-80, under the Patronage of the Empress. Georgi's Description de toutes les nations de l'Empire de Russie was the first ethnographic survey of the Russian Empire. It showed the world the great number and diversity of peoples inhabiting the empire and gave brief descriptions of their customs, economic life, religion, and dress (Whittaker).

ATKINSON, John Augustus and WALKER, K. James.
A Picturesque Representation of the Manners, Customs, Amusements of the Russians in one hundred coloured plates with an accurate explanation of each plate...
London, W. Bulmer, 1803- [1804].

First edition. Folio, 3 vols. in one; Vol. I half title, title, 5 ff. unnumbered comprising dedication, preface and list of plates in English and in French, engraved portrait of Alexander I by Scriven after Kugelgen; Vol. II, title, one leaf of text to each plate; Vol. III, title, one leaf of text to each plate, a total of 100 handcoloured aquatinted plates, (bound between vols. 33, 34, 33), full contemporary calf, gilt borders, inner gilt dentelles.
Abbey Travel 223; Colas 171; Lipperheide 1343; Prideaux, pp. 318-19; Tooley 72; Cicognara 1561; Gohen 104.

All the plates carry the signature drawn and etched by Augustus Atkinson as well as the addresses of the editors and the date of publication. Brunet and Vinet affirm, in referring to the catalogue Cicognara, that the work should include three portraits. As well as that of Czar Alexander I, there should be portraits of Catherine II and of Elisabeth. Colas states that he has only come across copies with one portrait and he assumes that the Cicognara description referred to a special copy to which two extra portraits had been added, not in fact belonging to this work. There was an issue with new titles dated 1812. Atkinson, the English artist, travelled extensively in Russia in the 1780s and 1790s.

BOSSOLI, Carlo.
The Beautiful Scenery and Chief Places of Interest
throughout the Crimea.
London, Day & Son, 1856.

Folio, lithographed title, 51 handcoloured lithographed plates
on 32 leaves, original green cloth, stamped in blind with gilt
title on upper cover.
Abbey Travel 239; Brunet I, 1130; Graesse I, 501.

Plates include Sebastopol; Balaklava; Prince Woronzoff's
Palace in Alupka; Tartar House in the village of Alupka;
Remains of the Genoese Forts at Ciufat-Kale; Kertch; the
Bosphorus. In uncoloured copies the fifty-two lithographs
appear on 30 leaves only some pages carrying two.
Virtually chromolithographs, the plates in this
sumptuously produced book, show when compared with
Hullmandel's work 17 years earlier in Boys's Paris, Ghent,
etc. 1839, something of the coarsening of effect in later,
more mechanical work (Abbey).

181

182
CARR, Sir John.
A Northern Summer or, Travels round the Baltic; through Denmark, Sweden, Russia, Prussia, and part of Germany, in the year 1804.
London, T. Gillet for Richard Phillips, 1805.

4to, title, dedication, contents pp. vii-xi; directions and errata, p. xii, text, pp. 1-480, 11 handcoloured aquatint plates, one folding, contemporary calf.
Abbey Travel 73; Cat. Russica No. C144; Prideaux pp. 218, 330.

Also published in Phillips' Collection of Voyages and Travels, 8vo, 1805-9 but three plates only. There was a French edition, 1808, German, 1806-8; and a Dutch, 1809-11. The plates may be by William Daniell. Daniell illustrated Carr's Tour through Holland... to Germany without signing them as usual, he famously only signed plates he had engraved if a friend was involved. Abbey considers that it is very probable that he also worked on these plates. Carr was knighted by the Duke of Bedford, Viceroy of Ireland on the publication of his Stranger in Ireland. Byron pilloried Carr in a cancelled passage of English Bards and Scotch Reviewers, and it is said begged, when he met Carr abroad, not to be put down on paper. Carr received £800 for this Northern Summer.

183
CHORIS, Ludovik Andreevich.
Voyage pittoresque autour du monde, avec des portraits de sauvages d'Amerique, d'Asie, D'Afrique, et des iles du Grand Ocean; des paysages, des vues maritimes, et plusieurs objets d'histoire naturelle; accompagne de descriptions par M. le Baron Cuvier, et M.A. de Chamisso, et d'observations sur les cranes humains, par M. le docteur Gall.
Paris, Impr. De Firmin Didot, 1822.

Both Choris and von Kotzebue went on very famous Russian expeditions to the Pacific. See fuller entries elsewhere in the catalogue.

184
CRIMEA. Guerra d'Oriente.
Florence, [c.1850s].

4to, 48 handcoloured lithographed plates, including portraits of the rulers, naval and military commanders and other notabilities involved in the Crimean war, as well as battle scenes and views, contemporary half calf.

An edition was published in Paris by Bulla Freres which had 60 plates lithographed by Gustave Dore.

185
DAMES, Captain T. Longworth.
Views in the Crimea.
London, Day & Son, August 22 1856.

Oblong folio, 6 handcoloured lithographed plates, contemporary green cloth.
Not in Abbey Travel; Blackmer; Atabey or other usual bibliographies.

A scarce work on the Crimea. This a presentation copy from Dames to Owen who also illustrated the Crimea, during the Crimean war, (see this catalogue below).

186
DICKINSON, publisher.
SEBASTOPOL. The Officers' Portfolio of Striking Reminiscences of the War.
[London], Dickinson Bros., [1855].

Folio, 22 handcoloured lithographed plates, plus two folding panoramic views, cloth backed boards, new ties, preserved in modern cloth box, morocco label.
Not in Abbey; Blackmer; Atabey or the other usual bibliographies, nor has it apparently appeared at auction.

A scarce and attractive work, showing groups of officers at leisure and in action during the siege of Sebastopol.

DROUVILLE, Gaspard de.
Voyage en Perse, pendant les annees 1812-13 par Gaspard de Drouville, Colonel de Cavalerie au service de S.Sm. l'Empereur de toutes les Russies, Chevalier de plusieurs ordres.
Paris, A la librairie nationale et etrangere, 1825.

Second edition. Two vols., 8vo, Vol. I, 256pp., introduction, text, table, Vol. II, 244pp. text, each vol. with half title and title, folding coloured lithographed map and 60 handcoloured lithographed plates by Motte, 4 double page, 20th century calf backed boards, spines gilt.
Colas 901; Lipperheide 1465.

The original plates, which were costume plates, were by the Russian master of the genre, Orlowsky. The first edition of this work was published in St. Petersburg, followed by several reissues. Drouville was in the service of the Czar of Russia. The plates are costume.

DUPLESSIS-BERTAUX, J.
Receuil des principaux Costumes militaires des Armees alliees.
Paris, Chez M.M. Galignani [et] Bance, 1816.

4to, three parts of text and 36 engraved handcoloured plates, contemporary quarter green calf, marbled sides, original printed pink wrappers bound in.
Colas 915.

This includes Russian military uniforms in particular, as well as some English and Prussian.

ECKERT, H.A.; MONTEN, D.; SCHELVER, F.

Les Armees d'Europe representees en groupes characteristiques composes et dessinees d'apres Nature…[Saemmtliche Truppen von Europa].
Munich, H.A. Eckert, D. Monten & F. Schelver [and] Wurzberg, Christian Weiss, [1838-43].

2 vols., 4to, lithographed general title, contents list, 369 (of 385) handcoloured lithographed plates, although it is difficult to assess exactly what is in this collection because there are a number of variants, and collections vary enormously, preserved in two contemporary Russian boxes, covered in green morocco with elaborate coloured morocco onlays; boxes lined with pink watered silk paper.
Colas 935; Lipperheide 2120.

The work is divided into two parts, the first devoted to German military uniforms, and the second part including other European armies. 128 of the plates in this section, according to Lipperheide, are devoted to Russian uniforms.

GAMBA, Jacques Francois, Chevalier.

Voyage dans la Russie Meridionale, et particulierement dans les Provinces situees au-dela du Caucase, fait depuis 1820 jusqu'en 1824.
Paris, Chez C.J. Trouve, Imprimeur-Libraire…1826.

First edition. 3 vols., 8vo and large 4to, Vol. I half title, title, 60 pp. introduction, (introduction), 444 pp. (text and index); Vol. II half title, title, 480pp. text and index, four folding maps and a folding table in the two text vols., and with 60 lithographed plates, 34 handcoloured, one double page map and two folding plates, 2 maps in atlas vol., contemporary calf over marbled boards.
BL; not in GL; Not in Blackmer; Atabey 475; Brunet II, 1473; Colas 1172.

A second edition appeared in 1826 with no differences. The plates illustrate the shores of the Black Sea and the Caucasus and include natural history subjects and views. The 34 coloured plates depict costume. Gamba made two voyages to Russia, that of 1820 at the orders of the Duc de Richelieu. He was consul at Tiflis in 1823 and there is a fine large plate of the capital city in this work. Almost all the plates state Chopin, del. There were 100 copies with the text vols. on vellum.

[GEISSLER, Christian Gottfried Heinrich.]

Russische Volk-Vergnugungen. Leipzig, Im Industrie Comptoir, [1801].

Folio, 4 aquatint plates handcoloured and mounted on grey paper, ruled in black ink and wash borders, the whole with text loose as issued and preserved in contemporary marbled paper folder.
Not in Colas; Lipperheide; or Abbey; NUC for Yale copy only.

An extremely rare set of these fine plates. Russian types were a favourite subject of foreign artists who visited or resided in Moscow and St. Petersburg. Importantly Geissler accompanied the expedition, sponsored by Catherine the Great and lead by Peter Simon Pallas, (for the account see elsewhere in this section of the catalogue), and his drawings appear in many of the ethnographic works subsequently published, famously his Cries of St. Petersburg.

GEISSLER, J.G.G. [and] HEMPEL, Frederic.

Tableaux Pittoresques des Moeurs, des Usages, et des Divertissements des Russes, Tartares, Mongols et autres Nations de l'Empire Russe [et] Mahlerische Darstellungen der Sitten, Gebraeuche und Lustbarkeiten bei den Russischen, Tartarischen, Mongolischen, und andern Voelkern im Russischen Reich…
Paris [Chez Fuchs, Chez Levrault], Leipzig [Chez Baumgaertner], [1804].

Four original parts in one vol., folio, title in French and German, descriptions of plates also in 2 languages, 40 handcoloured aquatint plates in an oval format showing scenes, games, and popular pastimes of the various regions of the Russian Empire, contemporary quarter green morocco over green cloth.
Colas 1208; Lipperheide 1344; Brunet III 94.

[GOUBAREV.]

Risunski k istorii leyb-buardii gusarskago Ego Velichestva polka [Dessins de l'Histoire du Regiment de Hussards de la Garde de S.M. l'Empereur, 1775-1859].
Saint Petersburg, 1859.

Folio, 1ff. title in Russian, 24 handcoloured lithographed plates numb. 1-24, by Konrad after the drawings of Goubarev, modern full red cloth, original blue wrappers bound in.
Colas 1269; Glasser, Catalogue des Principales Suites de Costumes Lithographes Francais, n. 719.

An important record of the uniforms of the Russian Imperial Guard; Regiment of Hussars over this period, commencing from the reign of Catherine the Great.

[HARDING, Edward.]

Costume of the Russian Empire.
London, T. Bensley, 1810.

Second edition. Large 4to, title in French, title in English, dedication, index of plates, 2ff. unnumbered, introduction in English and French, 70ff. unnumbered, text accompanying the plates, plates 5* and 14 without text, 20* does have accompanying text, 72 plates numbered 1 to 70 with these two bis plates, these all handcoloured stipple engravings, full contemporary green long-grain morocco, gilt fillets and

blindstamped borders.
Not in Abbey; Colas 704; Lipperheide 1342; Vinet 2321 for attribution to Harding.

Colas remarks that the impressions of these second edition plates seem to be as good as in the first edition of 1803. There are copies dated 1811. The majority of the plates of this work (except nine which represent groups) are taken from the collection of the highly influential collection of J.W. Georgi. (See also Alexander above.)

HOUBIGANT, A.G.
Moeurs et Costumes des Russes, Representes en 50 Planches Coloriees, Executees en Lithographie.
Paris, a la Librairie de Treuttel et Wurtz, Paris [and] Strassburg; de L'Imprimerie de Firman Didot, 1817.

Folio, half title, title, advertisement leaf, 20pp. description of the plates, 50 handcoloured lithographed plates numbered 1-50, Plates 1, 2, 3 and 18 signed by Be [Bellanger], quarter calf over paper covered boards, red morocco label.
Colas 1496; Lipperheide 1352 (lists 1821 edition), Brunet Vol. III, 27754.

Most of the plates are in part copies of those published by Atkinson. There were copies of this edition dated 1821 and there was a partial re-edition of the same year under the title of Receuil de trente Croquis representant des Scenes et Costumes Russes, Paris, Engelmann (30 plates).

JAMES, Rev. John Thomas.
Views in Russia, Sweden, Poland and Germany.
London, John Murray, 1826 [and Part V]; Davison White Friars, 1827.

Five original parts, folio, without title as issued, 20 coloured lithographed plates, original wrappers, preserved in modern cloth box.
Abbey Travel 23.

Abbey states that this work was obviously unfinished, for the three countries Sweden, Poland, Germany are crowded into the last part, while the whole of the first four parts with the exception of Plate 4 (Sweden) have been given over to Russia. The author, in his Preface, claims: "I…have lithographed [the plates] them myself, that they might not be subjected to such changes and variations of detail as too often occur when the original drawing and the print that is taken from it are furnished by different hands…In those prints which are given in chiaro-scuro, I have followed the example afforded by some of the artists at Vienna and Munich, many of whose productions are tinted with brown after the same fashion."

JOHNSTON, Robert.
Travels through Part of the Russian Empire and the Country of Poland; along the Southern Shores of the Baltic.
London, J.J. Stockdale, 1815.

Second edition. 4to, half title, title, dedication, contents, errata, plates, preface 1-xiv; text pp. 15-460, two maps, one of the North West part of Russia, 21 plates, nos. 1, 9, and 20 coloured line engraving, roulette and aquatint, no. 21 uncoloured woodengraving, the remainder handcoloured aquatints after Johnston by Stockdale, Lewis, Gledah, Dawe, Williams, Hill, contemporary half red straight grained morocco, spine gilt in compartments gilt, raised bands, m.e.
Cat. Russica, No. J557; Martin Hardie pp. 131-2; Prideaux, pp. 227, 341; Tooley no. 286.

The list of plates includes Skeleton of a Mammoth, although this is in fact a woodengraving in the text on pg. 125, which indicates that this is a second edition.
Plates include Russian Village near Moscow, Moscow, Kremlin, Borodino, Smolensk and a plate of Lithuanian Jews.

198

KOHLER, Gustav.
Ansichten von Muskau.
Gorlitz, verlag von Gustav Kohler, [1870s].

Oblong folio, series of 6 handcoloured lithographed plates, highly finished, preserved in quarter brown cloth over boards, with printed wrapper laid down on front boards.

One of the attractive collections of plates of Moscow for European travellers to the city.

199

[LAVISH CORONATION ALBUM.]
Description du sacre et du couronnement de leurs Majestes Imperiales l'Empereur Alexandre II et l'Imperatrice Marie Alexandrovna.
St. Petersburg, Academie Imperiales des Sciences, 1856.

First edition. Elephant folio, title printed in red and gold, text in French printed in bistre, chromolithographed frontispiece mounted on card as issued, 14 chromolithographed plates elaborately gilt, also mounted on card, two lithographed plans, one plate with two chromolithographed portraits within gilt borders, one chromolithograph in text, many other illustrations throughout text, tissue guards, half green morocco over cloth.

A superb de luxe publication appropriate to its subject, the coronation of the Czar Alexander II and his Tsarina Maria Alexandrovna. The lithographs printed by Lemercier are of the highest quality and also boast of being some of the largest to appear in a printed book.

LYALL, Robert.

The Character of the Russians, and a Detailed History of Moscow. Illustrated with numerous engravings. With a dissertation on the Russian language; and an Appendix. Containing tables, political, statistical, and historical; an account of the Imperial Agricultural Society of Moscow; a Catalogue of Plants found in and near Moscow; an essay on the origins and progress of architecture in Russia, &c. &c. London, T. Cadell, and A. & R. Spottiswoode, [and Edinburgh], 1823.

4to, title, dedication, contents, description of plates, plan of the City of Moscow in 1823, 23 plates, mostly handcoloured aquatints, the remainder uncoloured line-engravings, two folding, two wood engraved vignettes in text, plates signed, published by Thomas Cadell, those plates which are signed are Lavrof delt and E. Finden sculpt., 19th century blue calf gilt, armorial emblem on upper cover.
Abbey Travel 227; not in Tooley; Prideaux pp. 228, 343; Cat. Russica No. L1305.

Prideaux mentions only 12 plates, whereas in fact there are 14 aquatints, 13 of them coloured and 9 other plates. Views include the Kremlin, also included are costumes of Russia and genre scenes. According to his own account Lyall passed some of the best years of his life in the Russian empire. In 1815 he resided in St. Petersburg as physician to a nobleman's family, and he afterwards travelled to Kaluga with Mr Pollaratskii. From 1816 to 1820 he was attached to the establishment of the Countess Orlof-Tchesmenska at Ostrof, 16 miles from Moscow, in summer and in winter at the ancient capital. In 1821 he was attending General Natschokin at Semeonovskoye, near Moscow. In 1822 he travelled in a professional capacity through the Crimea, Georgia, and the southern provinces of Russia. He reached London from St. Petersburg in 1823, where he published this work.

This and his other later work both exposed what he saw as the corruption and immorality of the Russian nobles and officials, giving great offence in St. Petersburg, the Emperor disavowing Lyall's dedication of this work (DNB).

202

201

MILITARY UNIFORMS.
Galerie Militaire. Collection des Costumes Militaires de toutes les Nations.
Paris, Chez Dero-Becker, [1840-1855].

3 vols., 4to, original lithographed wrapper as title, 302 handcoloured lithographed plates, numbered 1 – 300 with two bis plates, 52 & 57, coloured lithographed by Coulon, contemporary green cloth.
Colas 1161.

202

[MORNAY.]
Une Annee de Saint-Petersbourg ou Douze Vues Pittoresques Prises dans Chaque Mois Representent les Places, Palais et Monuments les Plus Remarquables de Cette Capitale.
French edition [Paris, 1812].

Oblong folio, 12 handcoloured aquatint plates, map, contemporary half black calf over marbled boards.
Not in Abbey, Tooley or Hardie.

This edition without the set of 8 additional sledging plates as seen below.

203

MORNAY.
A Picture of Saint Petersburgh, represented in a Collection of Twenty interesting Views of the City, the Sledges, and the People. Taken on the spot at the twelve different months of the year: and accompanied with an Historical and Descriptive Account.
London, for Edward Orme, by J.F. Dove, 1815.

Folio, title, text, pp. 1-26; explanation of the 12 plates, pp. 27-28, 20 handcoloured aquatint plates, title uncoloured, duplicating label on original front cover, plates are signed Mornay del. Clark & Dubourg sculp, all imprinted Edward Orme, half burgundy morocco gilt.
Abbey Travel 226; Cat. Russica, No. P604; Martin Hardie, pg. 138; Prideaux, p. 345; Tooley (1954), No. 355.

The last eight plates show sledging scenes. One of the most beautiful plate books of St. Petersburg, the vision, architectural and engineering of Czar Peter the Great. His two aims in the project were defence against his neighbour Sweden and to bring European culture and scientific knowledge to Russia. Not only the exterior of the buildings, but the interiors, and the paintings and sculpture, provided an intentional and conspicuous display of splendour, aimed to give the Czar's message to all beholders. It was the political capital of the empire and the residence of all the foreign ambassadors.

204

[OFFICIERS, MARINIERS ET MARINS de la Division Navale de Kil-Bouron.]
Nos Souvenirs de Kil-Bouroun pendant l'Hiver dans le Liman du Dnieper, 1855-56.
Paris, Arthus Bertrand, [c. 1860].

Oblong folio, 17 tinted lithographed plates by Bayot, lithographed map, an atlas of plates without text as issued, original cloth.

Bertrand was one of the leading publishers of illustrated travel books in lithography in France at this time. Adolphe Jean Baptiste Bayot was one of his lithographers.

An interesting and reasonably exact copy for the German, Austrian and Russian armies of the collections of Eckert and Monten (see item above for original edition) and for the English army on that of Hullmandel, certain plates had been lithographed specially by V. Adam, Bastin, Bour, David, Finart, Lehnart, Le Pan, Pajol etc. There are numerous variants and several plates have been reprinted by Martinet-Hautecoeur, who continued publication of the "Galerie Militaire" under the title [Galerie Militaire. Deuxieme partie].

ORLOWSKI, G.
Russian Cries in Correct Portraiture from Drawings done on the Spot and now in the Possession of the Right Honourable Lord Kinnaird.
London, Edward Orme, 1809.

Small folio, handcoloured copper engraved title by J. Swaine, 8 handcoloured copper engraved plates unnum. by J. Godby after Orlowski, contemporary morocco-backed marbled boards.
Not in Abbey; Colas 2253; Lipperheide 1347; Hiler 67; de Jonghe 1930.

Plates comprise Peasants in Too Loo and "Cries", the Water Carrier, Kalatche Khorosh; Pasonda Khoroche, Skra Svija-Haviasfresh; Sbiten goriatchi – Tea Hot, Krafs Phoroche or Cantebery liquorgood; Miasnick or Butcher's meat. It seems that the initial G. for the author's name was an error, he was almost certainly Alexander Orlowski as below. Lord Kinnaird's library was renowned as one of the foremost private libraries of its time in Great Britain.

ORLOWSKI, Alexander.
Lithographic Costumes of Russia and Persia…
London, J.G. Ashley, [1821].

Folio, without title as issued, 10 coloured lithographed plates, two signed E. Purcell; Redman Lith., contemporary green cloth.
Abbey Travel 349.

The work appeared in original green wrappers and it is likely that they made three pairs or parts. Orlowski was born in Warsaw. According to Felix H. Man, his dates were 1780-1829 (Thieme u. Becker varies this by a few years). He went to Russia and became Court Painter at St Petersburg. When, in 1815, a lithographic press was set up there for printing documents, Orlowski took an interest in it and in 1816 produced his first published lithograph, the "Three Horsemen", which is probably also the first lithograph printed in Russia. By 1819 Orlowski had done some very large lithographs of Russian life, two of which Man reproduces. Orme's Russian Cries, above, gave the name G. Orlowski, but they would seem to be by the same artist (Abbey Travel).

Abbey 349 cites 6 plates. Redman was one of the early London lithographers, receiving the Silver Isis Medal of the Royal Society of Arts in 1819 for a lithograph on English stone. Hullmandel however did not go for his early lithographs to Redman because it is thought, of his determination to have his own press.

OWEN, Major C.H.
Sketches in the Crimea.
London, Paul and Dominic Colnaghi, 1856.

Oblong folio, coloured lithographed vignette title, and 5 coloured lithographed plates, three full-page, one folding, two images to one sheet, 19th century calf backed boards. Ogilby, Index to British Military Costume Plates, No. 688.

An attractive set of sketches showing the military in position in the Crimea, as well as the ports and docks described, a fresh approach, by Owen, who as well as an army officer was a member of the Royal Academy. The title vignette is of the Chapel in the Caves at Inkermann; three plates show the British troops, Dockyard and Barracks at Balaclava, lithographed by W.L. Walton; Monastery of St. George, two views on one sheet, this lithographed by E. Walker and Sebastopol from the 2nd Parallel right Attack, lithographed by R.M. Bryson.

PAJOL, Lieut. Col. Comte Charles Pierre Victor.
L'Armee Russe.
Paris, Imprimerie Auguste Bry, (Imprimerie A. Godard),
[1856].
Two parts in one vol., folio, total of 78 coloured lithographed
plates (56 costume plates, 21 plates of flags, medals, etc.),
contemporary half red morocco, gilt panelled black morocco
over marbled boards.
Colas 2260; Vinet 2328; Brunet IV-311; Lipperheide Q12 cites
incomplete copy; Glasser pp. 467 to 472 gives a description of
the plates.

Copies do exist on large paper with variant illustrations. This
work dedicated to the Russian Emperor was entirely the
work of Come Pajol. He was charged with a mission to
Russia and Poland which involved him for sixteen months.
The first part with 56 plates, contains all the army uniforms,
the first five plates are of portraits of Czar Nicholas and his
four sons. Nos. 13, 15, 27, 25, 31, 35, 40, 48, 50 and 51
were reworked to change the poses. Second part, consists of
25 images on 22 plates of the different organisations within
the army and show decorations, standards, pavilions,
colours etc. Plates by Lemercier, Godard, Aug. Bry. The price
was set at 125fr., but because of the book's scarcity, a
purchaser would have had to pay 200 fr. for it.

PALLAS, Pallas Simon.
Travels through the Southern Provinces of the Russian
Empire, 1793-94.
London, A. Strahan, T.N. Longman and O. Rees, T. Cadell
Jun. And W. Davies, and J. Murray and S. Highley, 1802-3.

2 vols., 4to, Vol. I, 51 plates, 1-25 stipple engravings,
handcoloured, nos. 26-51 stipple engravings with aquatint,
handcoloured, 16 folding, Vol. II 4 engraved maps, 3 folding,
two of the Black and Caspian Seas and the Crimea & Sea of
Azof, 29 vignettes, these squared up in line or line and stipple
engravings, many handcoloured, these split between the two
volumes, contemporary calf.
Abbey 222; Cat. Russica, No. P59; Prideaux pp. 220-1, 225,
347; Tooley (1954) Nos. 357-8.

The work was translated by F.W. Blagdon, the journalist and
author of the History of India (see elsewhere in this
catalogue). There was a second edition of the Pallas in 1812,
with according to Prideaux, extra plates, totalling 121. The
original German edition of the book was published in Leipzig
in 1799-1801, and the plates are copied from it. There was
also an edition in French. Most of the figure illustrations were
copied or used again some eight years later in John Stockdale's
publication of 1811, Costume of the Russian Empire. No.
246. Pallas also explored the flora of Western Siberia to
discover whether it had commercial possibilities, for dyes etc.
Karl Friedrich Knappe, for Pallas, produced an incomplete
Flora Rossica in St. Petersburg, 1784-88. It was a pioneering
work of Russian botany, but remained unfinished, comprising
only flowers found east of the Urals. The illustration were
made by Knappe. (Whittaker).

[PAUL I Petrovich (Tsar of Russia 1796-1801.]
Risunki sobstvennym voiskam pokoinago Imperatora
Paule I. Drawings of his own army by the Late Emperor
Paul I when his Highness was Grand Duke].
[St Petersburg], Lithographic Department of the Military
Settlement, 1835.

Small folio, 10 handcoloured lithographed plates, with early
manuscript inscriptions in German, contemporary dark green
calf gilt, blind and embossed central panel and border, inner
gilt dentelles.
Zaionchkovski 1715; not in Colas, Hiler, Lipperheide or
Obal'ianinoy.

Czar Paul with relation to his army was a controversial
disciplinarian, his military reforms being reversed by his
successor Alexander I, including the uniforms of his reign.

PAULY, Theodore de.
Description Ethnographique des Peuples de la Russie.
Saint Petersburg, F. Bellizard, (plates printed as follows: Berlin, Winkelmann; Munich, Kuhn; Paris, Charpentier/Lemercier),1862
First edition. Folio, xiv pp., half title, title, dedication to Czar Alexander II, preface by Ch. De Baer, indexes, 147ff. text numbered by regions, 155pp. (Peuples Indo-Europeens), 30pp., (Peuples du Caucase), 78pp. (Peuples Ouralo-Altaiques), 16pp. (Peuples de la Siberie Orientale), 16pp. (Peuples de l'Amerique Russe), 63 chromolithographed plates, map, chart, modern maroon cloth backed marbled boards.
Colas 2292; Lipperheide 1367; Vinet 2329.

"The work is very rare and one of the most beautiful for the different costumes of the peoples of Russia" – Colas. Plates lithographed after drawings by Karpoff, C. Huhn, N. Sauerweid, F. Teichel, Viale, Zakharoff, etc.

PINKERTON, Robert.
Russia: or, Miscellaneous Observations on the Past and Present State of that Country and its Inhabitants…
London, Seeley & Sons, Hatchard & Son, 1833.

8vo, 2ll., half title, title, 4ll preface, 486pp. text, 1ll. unnumbered (index), 8 handcoloured lithographed plates, showing costumes, and public entertainment, original cloth-backed boards.
Cat. Russica, No. P668; Abbey Travel 230; Colas 2395; Lipperheide 1356; Tooley 380.

The work was compiled from notes made on the spot, during travels, at different times, by Pinkerton who was in the service of the Bible Society, and was a resident of many years in that country. Plates include a hawker of sacred pictures, or icons; Svaika, a favourite game of the Moujicks; Village Amusements of the Russians.

[PLUCHART, Alexandre.]
Saint Petersbourg. Nouvelle Collection de Quarante-Deux Vues de Saint-Petersbourg et de ses Environs.
[Saint Petersburg, Pluchart, and Paris, 1824].

Oblong folio, 42 handcoloured lithographed plates of the city, original illustrated boards, rebacked in calf.

Lithography in Russia was well established by this date and publisher Pluchart capitalised on the swell of tourists to St. Petersburg and Russia following the relatively new peace in Europe. St. Petersburg was firmly established as the capital of Russia and also an artistic and scientific capital in European terms, thanks to the enormous influx of Europeans to the city. Pluchart produced a series of illustrated publications with the foremost views of the city, with varying numbers of plates. This with its 42 plates was at the top end of his market. As well as being commercial, the plates were also attractive, showing the picturesque landmarks of the city.

PORTER, Sir Robert Ker.
Travelling Sketches in Russia and Sweden.
London, T. Gillet, 1809.

First edition. 2 vols., Vol. I, title, preface, contents, list of plates, Vol. II title, contents, text pp. 1-296; 41 plates, an uncoloured etching, 9 uncoloured aquatints tinted by hand with a sepia wash, and the remainder handcoloured aquatint vignettes, these divided between two vols., 1-28 and 29-41, the first 28 plates relate to Russia, including the Urals and Moscow, contemporary full diced calf.
Colas 2407; Lipperheide 1346; Tooley (1954) 382; Prideaux, pp. 225, 227 and 347.

There was a second edition in 1813, published by John Stockdale (Cat. Russica No. P1036). For biographical details see below. The majority of the plates are of Russia, with those of Sweden in the second volume, reflecting Porter's overwhelming interest in Russia.

PORTER, Sir Robert Ker.
Travels in Georgia, Persia, Armenia, Ancient Babylonia, during the Years 1817, 1818, 1819, and 1820.
London, for Longman, Hurst, Rees, Orme and Brown, 1821-22.

First edition. 2 vols., 4to, Vol. I, xxiii pp, title, dedication, preface, list of Persian rulers, index, 720pp. text, 1 unn. ff., line engraved frontispiece by Fry after Porter, 82 plates, uncoloured line and stipple engravings 1-57; uncoloured line, and aquatints, 5 handcoloured plates, these all split between two vols., engraved by Heath and Clark after Porter, contemporary diced Russia gilt.
Abbey Travel 359; Tooley 384; Brunet IV, 828.

Several of these plates are handcoloured as mentioned above and show the costumes of the areas visited. This very interesting work describes travels through Russia and the Caucasus to Persia, returning by way of Asia Minor to Constantinople, Thrace, the Balkans and Bucharest. Porter was an artist and diplomat. In 1804 he had been appointed as historical painter to the Czar of Russia. He decorated the Admiralty Hall at St. Petersburg with some vast historical paintings. During his residence in the capital he won the affections of a Russian princess, Mary, daughter of Prince Theodore von Scherbatoff, but some hitch in the courtship necessitated his leaving Russia. He returned in 1811 and in 1812 triumphantly married his Russian Princess. He was subsequently received in Russian military and diplomatic circles, and became well acquainted with the events of 1812-13. In 1817 he started from St. Petersburg on a long journey through the Caucasus to Teheran, then southwards by Ispahan to the site of the ancient Persepolis, where he made many valuable drawings. He then proceeded to Baghdad and on to Scutari. This account of these travels was well received: "This huge book, which is full of interest and is a great advance upon his previous volumes of travel, was illustrated by bold drawings of mountain scenery, works of art and antiquities" (DNB).

[RECHBERG. Charles Comte de and DEPPING, George Bernhard.]
Les Peuples de la Russie, ou Description des Moeurs, Usages et Costumes des Diverses Nations de l'Empire de Russie.
Paris, De l'Imprimerie de D. Colas (Treuttel et Wurtz), 1812-13.

2 vols., folio, dedication signed by Rechberg, 2ff, half title and title, 13pp. preface, 61 unn. leaves of text and two leaves of indexes, 48 handcoloured aquatint plates (including title) engraved by A. Manz, Scotnikoff, Melnikoff, I. Laminit, X. Wagner, Hesse, Gros, Adam and Coqueret after drawings by E. Karnejeff , the text is by Rechberg and revised by G.B. Depping, contemporary quarter calf, preserved in modern linen boxes.
Colas 2491; Lipperheide 1348; Brunet IV, 582; Vinet 2329.

There are uncoloured copies of this work and those heightened by hand as is this copy.
   Lipperheide lacks plate 18, "Cosaques de Don", replaced by "Montagne de glace a Tobolsk."

RUSSIAN COSTUME. Russische Kostume und Landertrachten. In Illuminierten Zeichnungen.
n.p., [c. 1780].

Folio, 84 magnificently handcoloured plates, contemporary half calf gilt, armorial device on upper cover.
Not in Colas or Lipperheide.

A scarce set of fine costume plates of the various regions of Russia.

TIMM, W.
Costumes Russes dessinees d'apres Nature et lithographies par W. Timm...
Moscow and St Petersburg, Daziario, [Lemercier, Paris], [1843-1844].

Oblong folio, lithographed title in purple and gilt, 28 coloured lithographed plates, (nos. 1-24, 4 unn.), contemporary green boards, gilt lettered on upper cover, late straight grained morocco backing.
Colas 2880; Lipperheide 1360.

Plates captioned in French or in French & Russian.

WELTMANN, A[leksander Fornich].
Description du Nouveau Palais Imperial du Kremlin de Moscou.
Moscow, Imprimerie d'Alexandre-Semen, 1851.

Oblong 4to, [4], 38pp.text, 9 chromolithographed plates, 12 photographic plates, all images mounted on card, 2 plans,

separate text in French, translation by Baron Leon de Bode, in original coloured lithographed wrappers, contemporary folder, orange cloth and yellow paper sides, from the Hofbibliothek zu Donaueschingen.
Brunet V, 1432.

Weltmann, a popular writer in 1830s and 1840s, influenced the new generation of writers, Pushkin, Gogol and Dosteovsky. These plates were commissioned by Tsar Nicolas I in 1838, and was finished in 1851. It included the Kremlin Palace, with the Moscow Armoury and state rooms attached. These fine chromolithographed plates form an important record of the newly completed Imperial complex and include interiors.

Indian Subcontinent

220

ACKERMANN, R.
[Costumes of India.]
London, 1828.

Small 8vo, 42 handcoloured aquatint costume plates, modern half brown calf, marbled paper sides, with the bookplate of Major Abbey, although not in Abbey catalogue.
Not in Abbey; Colas or Lipperheide.

221

ANDRASY, Count Emanuel.
Reise des Grafen Emanuel Andrasy in Ostindien aus dem Ungarishen ubersetzt.
Ceylon, Java, China and Bengalen.
Budapest, Hermann Geibel, 1859.

First German edition. Oblong folio, half title, 16 handcoloured lithographed plates after Andrasy by Ciceri, some uncoloured illustrations in text, contemporary half morocco over original cloth, gilt vignette on upper cover of hunting elephant and man shooting from the Howdah.
Nissen ZBI 111; not in de Silva; Abbey or Tooley.

Scarce. Count Emanuel Andrasy was a Hungarian nobleman who fled Budapest when it was taken over in 1849 by the Austrians. He travelled in the east, visiting Ceylon, India, Java and the China coast. His work appeared first in Hungarian in 1853. Also published in a similar format were Les Chasses et le Sport en Hongrie (1857) See elsewhere in this catalogue.

The plates show sporting scenes in Ceylon (Sri Lanka), (6), Java (3), India (5), Hong Kong (1) and Egypt (1). The majority are of big game hunting for elephant, tiger, rhinoceros, stag and crocodile.

ATKINSON, J[ames].
Sketches in Afghaunistan.
London, Henry Graves and Company, 1842.

First edition, folio, lithographed pictorial title, lithographed dedication, descriptive text for the 25 lithographed plates by Louis and Charles Haghe after Atkinson, title and plates mounted on card and loose as issued in original morocco backed pebbled cloth folder, gilt ruled, label gilt on morocco on upper cover.
Tooley(1954) 73; Abbey Travel 508; Colas 173; Lipperheide 1493.

The publishers issued Hart's Characters and Costumes of Afghanistan the following year (1843) as a companion volume to this work. An 8vo edition of Atkinson's work was published by Allen with a map, bound in cloth for 10s. 6d. Atkinson's original profession was surgeon and he returned to this after his return from England in 1833. He had originally been invited to Calcutta by Governor General Lord Minto and given the appointment of assistant assay master for the mint. His work there was broken by a short period as Deputy Professor in Persian at the Fort William College and by a visit to England. In 1838 he was appointed superintending surgeon to the army of the Indus and accompanied it on its march to Kabul, but was relieved in ordinary course of routine shortly after the surrender of Dost Mohammad, and returned to Bengal in 1841 and thus escaped the fate which befell the army of occupation. His text on the Expedition into Afghanistan was considered a valuable and interesting personal narrative with this supplementary series of lithographed drawings, serving to complete the picture of what was then an unexplored country. At once a scholar and popular writer, James Atkinson holds an honourable place among the pioneers of oriental research. Most of the plates are views, but there are some representing the costumes of Cabul.

BELNOS, MRS. S.C.
Twenty-four plates illustrative of Hindoo and European Manners in Bengal.
London, Smith and Elder and Paris, A. Colin, [c. 1832].

First edition. Small folio, lithographed pictorial title, 24 handcoloured lithographed plates after Mrs. Belnos by A. Colin and J.J. Belnos, leaf of descriptive text to each plate, (recto in French, verso in English), contemporary calf over green papered boards, gilt lettered direct, original pictorial wrappers bound in as title.
Abbey Travel 458 for a later issue; Colas 292.

A scarce work. This work with this imprint would appear to be the issue described in Abbey. It is possible that Mrs. Belnos was an Indian and also that the plates for this edition were printed in Paris. It is thought that the lithographer of these plates, Jean-Jacques Belnos, was probably her husband. He is given in Thieme U. Becker as a lithographer and artist.

A. Colin d'après M.ᵉ Belnos.

Lith. d. J. J. Belnos.

Fête du Churruck Poojah.   Feast of the Churruck Poojah.

BLAGDON, Francis William [William DANIELL, Francis Swain WARD and James HUNTER].
A Brief History of Ancient and Modern India From the Earliest Periods of Antiquity to the termination of the late Mahratta War [title to letterpress].
London, Edward Orme, 1802-1805 [but c. 1828].

Large folio, handcoloured stipple engraved portrait frontispiece of Tippoo Sultan, two handcoloured engraved pictorial additional titles, handcoloured stipple-engraved folding plate of "Judges and Court Officials", and 64 handcoloured aquatint plates, polished half calf, spine ornately gilt in compartments, label on upper cover.
This work includes William Daniell and Colonel Francis Ward's Twenty-Four Views in Hindostan and James Hunter's Picturesque Scenery in the Kingdom of Mysore.

These were originally published separately, then in parts 1802-1805 and then as one volume from 1805.
Abbey Travel 425 (cf. 424); cf. Lipperheide 1478; cf. Tooley (1954) 93 & 275.

Blagdon was a journalist and author. His Brief History of Ancient and Modern India came out in 3 4to vols. It was reissued in 1813 as an appendix to Captain Thomas Williamson's European in India, and in 1806. He was responsible for several other publications and later after coming into conflict with William Cobbett he published a prospectus of Blagdon's Weekly Political Register which was to be in the style of Cobbett's Register, but it never seems to have appeared. There is another issue of this work in this collection with two parts by Hunter and Blagdon).

TIPPOO SULTAN.

From an original Picture in the possession of

The Marquis Wellesley.

Published & Sold 1805 by Edw.¹ Orme His Majesty's Printseller Bond Street London.

225

BROUGHTON, Thomas Duer.
Letters written in a Mahratta Camp during the year 1809, descriptive of the Character, Manners, Domestic Habits, and Religious Ceremonies, of the Mahrattas, With Ten Coloured Engravings, from drawings by a Native Artist...
London, John Murray, 1813.

First edition. 8vo, half title, 10 handcoloured aquatint plates, including frontispiece, etched and handcoloured by J.A. Atkinson, T. Baxter, and Moses after the original drawings by Deen Alee, and each with the imprint of J. Murray, Albemarle Street, contemporary half calf over boards.
Tooley 114; Abbey Travel 433; Colas 454; Lipperheide 1480.

Broughton was sent to India as a cadet on the Bengal establishment. He was actively engaged at the siege of Seringapatam in 1799 and was afterwards appointed Commandant of the Cadet Corps, and in 1802 Military Resident with the Mahrattas. For a short time previous to the restoration of Java to the Dutch he held the command of that island.

226

[BURNOUF, M.E. and JACQUET, Eugene.]
L'Inde Francaise ou collection de dessins lithographies representant les divinites, temples, costumes, physiognomies, meubles, armes et ustensiles, ...des peuples hindous qui habitent les possessions francaises de l'Inde, et en general la Cote de Cormandel et le Malabar.
Paris, Chabrelie, editeur, 1827-1835].

First edition. 2 vols., folio, 144 handcoloured lithographed plates by C. Motte and others after various artists, each with explanatory leaf of text, contemporary half red morocco, spine gilt in compartments, raised bands.
Colas 490; Vicaire I, 979; Brunet I, 1412; not in Lipperheide.

A scarce work which has appeared only four times at auction in the past thirty years, none of these copies with the appendix. Was originally produced in 25 original parts, each with 6 coloured lithographed plates. Illustrated and published by M.M. Geringer and Chabrelie, with text by Burnouf. Geringer's name was on all the prospectuses for the work, and he seems to have been the principal collaborator (Colas).

227

BUTLER, John.

A Sketch of Assam: with some account of the Hill Tribes. By an Officer in the Hon. East India Company's Bengal Native Infantry in civil employ. With Illustrations from Sketches by the Author.
London, Smith, Elder & Co., 1847.

8vo, title, verso with imprint: London, Printed by Stewart and Murray, advertisements, general folding map of Assam, and 17 plates, Plate 10 an uncoloured woodcut, others handcoloured lithographs, woodcut vignettes, contemporary marbled board, backed with tan linen.
Abbey Travel 471.

As well as a plate of a mangoe fly and a long horned beetle, and other natural historical subjects, there is also a plate of buffalo shooting, and costumes and types of Assam, together with an Assam hunter's equipment, cross-bow, quiver etc.

228

CAMPBELL, Lieut. Col. J.

Excursions Adventures and Field-Sports in Ceylon; its Commercial and Military Importance and numerous Advantages to the British Emmigrant.
London, 1843.

2 vols., 8vo, 8 coloured plates, seven folding, 9 uncoloured plates, two maps, one folding, contemporary polished calf, narrow gilt border, spines gilt in compartments, raised bands, g.e., bookplate of Christopher Turner Stoke Rochford Library. Not in de Silva.

Apart from BMC and Library of Congress, this does not seem to be in any lists, although six copies have come up for auction in recent years.

CARPENTER, Percy.
Hog Hunting in Lower Bengal.
W. Thacker & Co., Day & Son, 1861.

First edition. Large folio, tinted lithographed title with handcoloured vignette and 8 handcoloured lithographed plates, all mounted on card with captions and ruled border printed in gilt, contemporary morocco backed cloth gilt lettered direct on upper cover, in modern morocco back cloth covered box.
Czech p.44; Schwerdt I, p. 97.

Carpenter notes in the introduction that the drawings were taken from sketches and notes made during a meet held by the Calcutta Tent Club in March 1860 on the Sowerra Burrea Plains, near Tumluk, 50 miles S.E. from Calcutta. The hunting party consisted of 15 attendants, numbering around 60 people. There were also eleven elephants to act as beaters in the long grass, jungle and woods on the plain. The hunt lasted three days during which time they killed thirty seven hogs. "One of the few books on pigsticking and very difficult to find in good condition" (Schwerdt).

COLEBROOK, Robert Hyde.
Twelve Views of Places in the Kingdom of Mysore, the Country of Tippoo Sultan.
Second edition. London, for Edward Orme, 1805.

2 vols., large oblong folio, 12 handcoloured aquatint plates by John William Edy after R.H. Colebrook, within colour washed borders, without title, descriptive letterpress interleaved with plates, subscription list, one name added in manuscript ordering six copies, the dedicatee Cornwallis took three, 19th century half brown morocco over marbled boards.
Abbey Travel 419 (for note).

Colebrook the first great Sanskrit scholar of Europe was the son of Sir George Colebrooke, the head of an old and wealthy firm of bankers. He served in the East India Company for 32 years, and was glad to be appointed finally as assistant collector at Tirhut in 1786, happy to leave Calcutta and the heavy drinking bouts of the bucks. He himself had a strong head and despised those who lost theirs. He accused Warren Hastings of being the author of these debaucheries. He made a minute study of the state of husbandry in Bengal, his findings being privately printed in 1795. It opposed the renewal of the company's monopoly, and advocated free-trade principles. The work gave offence to the directors, and was not published in England.

By the time Colebrook arrived at Nagpur in 1799 events had forestalled him; Seringapatam had fallen and Tippoo Sultan was dead, and the jealousy and suspicion of the Mahrattas had been so excited by the proceedings of the English in the distribution of the Mysore dominions, that any attempts at conciliation were useless, and an alliance was out of the question. Colebrook had been sent to Mysore to carry out Marquis Wellesley's policy by inducing the Rajah of Berar to join the defensive alliance with the Company against the power or Scindia, who threatened to support Tippoo. After many delays, Colebrooke left Nagpur in 1801, with a sense of unavoidable failure. The subsequent struggles with the Mahratta states, ending in the victories of Assaye and Argaum, and the annexation of Cuttack, showed the temper which the Mysore proceedings had provoked. His four volume Digest had been published (Calcutta, 1798) and brought him remuneration, recognition and advancement.

231

DANIELL, Thomas.
[Views in Calcutta.]
[Calcutta, 1786-1788.]

First edition. Oblong folio, 12 handcoloured aquatint views, loose as issued without title or text, trimmed to within half an inch of the image and mounted on museum board; mounts on guards, modern half navy morocco, with matching label on upper cover.
Abbey Travel 492; Archer p. 12; Foster, pg. 21; Sutton, pp. 20-3; and No. 8 (p. 155).

A very rare set of plates which were published at 12 gold Mohurs to subscribers and 18 to non-subscribers. Daniell was very likely teaching himself the new art of aquatint engraving when he undertook these views, which were handcoloured by local artists under his supervision. When he finished the twelve plates in November 1788 he wrote to Ozias Humphry. "The Lord be praised, at length I have finished my 12 views of Calcutta. The fatigue I have experienced in this undertaking has almost worn me out… It will appear a very poor performance in your land, I fear. You must look upon it as a Bengalee work. You know I was obliged to stand Painter, Engraver, Coppersmith, Printer and Printers Devil myself, it was a devilish undertaking but I was determined to see it through at all events" (Abbey). The first announcement of this work came only a few months after the Daniells reached India, in the form of an advertisement in the Calcutta Chronicle of 17 July 1786. In May the following year an announcement stated, "Mr Daniell has completed six of the views and will deliver impressions as soon as possible". Sutton does remark that although classed as aquatints by all his contemporaries, Daniell's plates are more nearly etchings, with some crude attempts at aquatinting, and what appears to be actual scraping of the plates. The attempt to apply aquatint may have been partly dictated by Thomas's desire to rival and outstrip Hodges, whose Select Views in aquatint probably began to appear in England, in May 1785. Copies of the first part therefore could have reached Calcutta before the Daniells' arrival.

DANIELL, Thomas and William.
Oriental Scenery.
London, Thomas Daniell, 1795-1799.

Large folio, Parts 1, 2 and first half of 3, (of 6), these 3 parts each with additional pictorial aquatint titles and 60 aquatint plates (of 144), all handcoloured, later 19th century green morocco ornately gilt bordered, spine gilt in compartments, raised bands.
Abbey Travel 420; Sutton 13; Tooley 172; Franklin pp. 28-29; Prideaux, pp. 94, 244.

This was the great work of the Daniells, uncle and nephew, which is considered the finest set of prints ever published of India. They spent about nine years, from 1765-94 making their studies, sketches and drawings of the scenery, architecture and antiquities, which then took a further thirteen years to publish their remarkably accurate aquatints. It was a costly work at the time and was offered at 200 guineas, which can be compared with the price of £100 for the handcoloured lithographs of David Roberts's Holy Land, issued 50 fifty years later. The work was enormously influential in forming the European vision of India and the vogue for Indian-inspired architecture in England, which can be seen in the works of Humphrey Repton and John Nash among others.

DANIELL, William and DAVIS, Samuel.
Views in Bootan from the drawings of Mr Davis. Respectfully inscribed to Warren Hastings Esqr. Late Governor General of India...
London, William Daniell, 1813.

Oblong folio, engraved title, 14 lines of preface or introduction, 6 leaves of descriptive text of the plates, double column, each verso blank, 6 handcoloured aquatint plates by William Daniell after S. Davis, modern full red period style morocco, gilt border, spine gilt raised bands.
Abbey Travel II, 434; Sutton p. 141.

According to Sutton these are probably the rarest of Williams Daniell's sets of engravings. Samuel Davis was a great friend of William and Thomas Daniell and the latter therefore signed the three plates. He told Farrington that he only signed his engravings after other artists, when that artist was a friend of his. Some of Davis's sketches of Bhutan were also engraved by William Daniell for the Oriental Annual, 1834-9 (Sutton p. 141).

232

D'OYLY, Sir Charles.
Views of Calcutta and Its Environs.
London, Dickinson, 1848.

Large folio, lithographed title, 25 handcoloured lithographed plates, plates lithographed by W. Robert & Lowes Dickinson, plus frontispiece by Dickinson, original half morocco, gilt ruled and decorated, title within architectural frame, spines gilt, raised bands.
Abbey Travel 497; Tooley 187.

D'Oyly seems to have been an amateur artist of some merit. He was also a man of character; though his forebears had a reputation as wasters. He seems to have emerged from India, a graveyard then both of men and souls, respected by all. An obituary in the Gentleman's Magazine recalls that a contemporary called him "one of the most elegant, gentlemanlike, handsome, and accomplished men of his day". As to his artistic powers, according to Cotton, based on Heber, he had had the advantage in about 1808 of regular lessons from a very able artist of the name of Chinnery, who was then in India. It will be noticed that several of his lithographs in the Behar Amateur Lithographic Scrap Book were after sketches by Chinnery.

D'OYLY, Sir Charles.
Costumes of India.
[Patna], Behar Private Lithographic Press, [c. 1850].

Small 4to, 12 handcoloured lithographed costume plates, trimmed and mounted each within lithographic border, upper cover with uncoloured lithograph, similarly trimmed and mounted on boards.
Apparently not in Abbey.

This work from the Behar Private Lithographic Press does not accord with any of the Scrap Book titles listed in Abbey. Sir Charles apparently set up his amateur lithographic press in 1828. The first lithographic press in India may have been the Asiatic Lithographic Press, Calcutta, which in 1825 printed Grierson's Twelve Select Views of the Seat of War. It is implied in a note in the work that this was the first time in India that lithography had been applied to views. As is discussed in the Notes to No. 403, that this probably means that, as in many other cases, lithography had been introduced to India for copying maps and documents. It is also perhaps possible to deduce from archive material that D'Oyly's first sketches may have been lithographed at the Asiatic Press. However, a quantity of his work did appear from his own press.

D'OYLY, Charles; WILLIAMSON, Capt. Thomas; BLAGDON, Francis William.
The European in India; from a Collection of Drawings by Charles D'Oyly, Esq. Engraved by J.H. Clark and C. Dubourg with a preface and copious descriptions.
London, Edward Orme, 1813.

Tall 4to, half title, title, preface 11pp., list of plates, 20 handcoloured aquatint plates, original drab boards.
Abbey Travel 435; Tooley 185; Archer p. 33; Colas 887; Martin Hardie pp. 132-33; Tooley (1954).

Tooley evidently considers that this book was published before the Costume and Customs of Modern India, No. 440 Abbey, which uses the same plates (with some variation in the frames which are washed in grey and pink, instead of yellow), but which does not contain Blagdon's Brief History. It is likely that there was a second edition of Costume and Customs in 1830. Blagdon's Complete History, illustrated with two plates, also appears with Daniell and Ward's 24 Views in Hindoostan and Hunter's Picturesque Scenery in the Kingdom of Mysore in Orme's part publication of 1802-5.

EDEN, Emily.
Portraits of the Princes and People of India.
London, J. Dickinson & Son, 1844.

Folio, lithographed pictorial title with handcoloured vignette, and 24 handcoloured mounted lithographed plates on card by Lowes Dickinson and printed by C. Hullmandel, with 27 images, lithographed plate list, descriptive text leaf to each plate, loose as issued in later morocco backed cloth folder, ties.
Not in Abbey; Colas 936; Pal & Deleijia pp. 132-133.

Emily Eden, novelist and traveller, was the sister of George Eden, second Baron of Auckland, who became Governor General of India. She and her sister Frances Eden accompanied their brother to India and acted as his hostesses at Government House and on his travels through India during his term of office, 1835-42. On her return to London, Emily Eden published this work and in 1866 followed "Up the Country. Letters written to her Sister from the Upper Provinces of India..." In these volumes the visits between Lord Auckland and Runjeet Singh are recorded with minute particulars, making important and interesting reading.

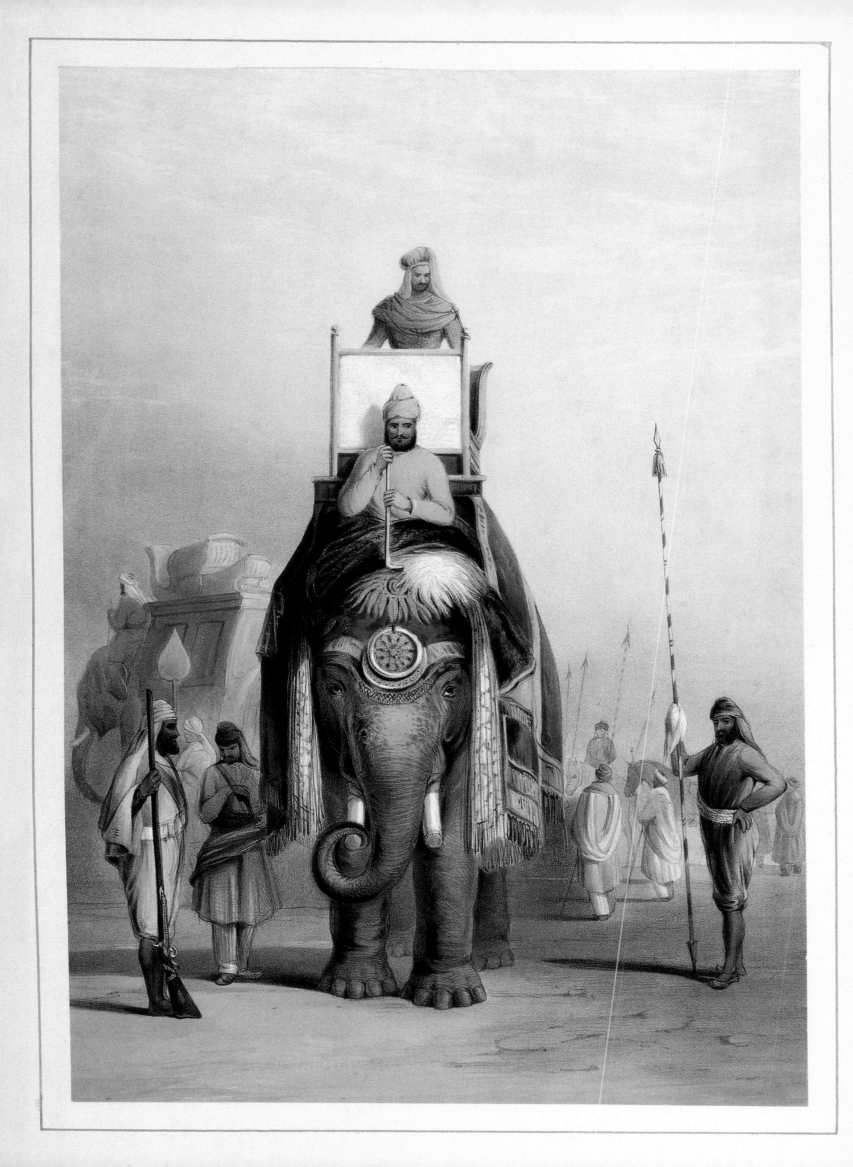

238

EDWARDS, William.
Sketches in Scinde from drawings by Lieut. Wm. Edwards.
[London, Graves], 1846.

Folio, lithographed title, 9 handcoloured lithographed plates by Haghe and Williams, plan of Scinde, one leaf of text, one dedication leaf and plan, all mounted on card within ink ruled borders, loose as issued, with inscription to S. Jackson, "Presentation copy/S. Jackson Esqre. With his Pupils very kind regards April 1846", preserved in modern cloth covered box.
Abbey Travel II, 469; Tooley 193.

Plates are views of the buildings of Fort Hyderabad and include the Main Guard & Government House; View from the Round Tower; Entrance to the Town of Schewan, and Lal Shah Baz's Tomb; the Fortress of Deyrah.

239

ELPHINSTONE, Hon. Mountstuart.
An Account of the Kingdom of Caubul, and its Dependencies in Persia, Tartary, and India; comprising a View of the Afghan Nation, and a History of the Dooraunee Monarchy.
London, Longman, Hurst, Rees, Orme and Brown, 1815.

First edition. 4to, two engraved maps handcoloured in outline (one large and folding), 13 handcoloured aquatint plates, later half calf over marbled boards, spine raised bands gilt ruled, m.e.
Abbey 504; Tooley 209; Colas 960; Lipperheide 1483.

One of the important works on Afghanistan. Elphinstone became the Governor of Bombay and he can be credited for laying the foundations of much of the administrative and education infrastructure of the British Raj. In 1808 he was appointed ambassador to the Afghan Court at Kabul and Elphinstone draws heavily on his journey in Afghanistan, Baluchistan and the Punjab. His attention was drawn to the costume and customs of the people he encountered and many of these are shown in his work. In fact, as Abbey points out, three of these were drawn by Lieutenant R.M. Grindlay, see his own famous work The Scenery, Costumes and Architecture of India, 1826-30 below.

EYRE, Lieut. Vincent.
Portraits of the Cabul Prisoners.
[London, c. 1844].

8vo, 2 vols., 32 handcoloured lithographed plates, each plate titled by hand in ink on mount, original cloth portfolio, morocco titling label on upper cover [together with the text vol.]. 4to, in original green cloth, central vignette gilt of Afghan fighters, spine gilt lettered and preserved in modern green linen box together with text, this in original cloth.
Not in Abbey.

An account of the devastating retreat of the British army from Afghanistan, their losses and the number of those captured, (see elsewhere in the catalogue an account of the siege of Jellabad).

FERGUSSON, James.
Picturesque Illustrations of Ancient Architecture in Hindostan.
London, J. Hogarth, George Barclay, 1848.

Folio, sketch map of India, frontispiece p.17. Bowlee at Boondee, lithographed title, and 22 other tinted lithographed plates, nos. 3,4,6 &7 with some colour in addition. No. 5 one tint only coloured, no. 10 one tint only, plates drawn and lithographed by T.C. Dibdin, from a sketch by J. Fergusson Esqr. and Printed by M.& N. Hanrart, woodengraved vignettes in text, contemporary half red morocco, gilt ruled, spine raised bands, gilt lettered, edges red.
Abbey Travel 480.

This work was first published in 1848 with the lithographed title dated 1847, as in the British Museum, the letterpress title the same as here. Fergusson was a writer on architecture. He travelled to India to take up a place in a firm of which his elder brother was a partner, Fairlie, Fergusson, & Company, merchants in Calcutta. Soon after his arrival in India at an early age he started an indigo factory on his own account, and as he fortunately left the parent company before its failure he was able in about ten years' time to retire from business with a moderate competency, and to carry out an early resolution of devoting himself to archaeological studies. His antiquarian enthusiasm was boundless and he was a skilled draughtsman with the camera lucida, much in vogue at this time, following its use with success by the Daniells. His last visit to India was in 1845, but before this chiefly between 1835 and 1842, he had made the lengthened tours in India which are shown in the map in this work. Schliemann was to dedicate his great work, "Tiryns" to Fergusson, as "the historian of architecture, eminent alike for his knowledge of art and for the original genius which he has applied to the solution of some of its most difficult problems".

FIEBIG, Frederick.
[Panoramic Views of Calcutta].
Calcutta, T. Black, 1847.

Small oblong folio, 6 handcoloured lithographed plates, Nos. 1-6 with captions, images within double black rule, modern black morocco backed boards, upper cover gilt lettered.
Not in Abbey or Tooley.

An apparently scarce work with no copies at auction recorded on ABPC. Often the case with Calcutta printing, only few copies were published.

FITZCLARENCE, Lt. Col. George Augustus, Earl of Munster.
Journal of a Route across India, through Egypt, to England...1817...1818.
London, John Murray, 1819.

First edition. 4to, 2 maps, one folding, 9 handcoloured aquatint plates by R. Havell and Son, 8 engraved plates and plans, original boards, later rebacked in cloth, spine gilt lettered direct.
Abbey Travel 519; Gay 2025; Ibrahim-Hilmy, Vol. I, pg. 233; Prideaux, pp. 247, 336; Tooley (1954), 222; Wilson pg. 71.

Fitzclarence served in the 24th light dragoons under the command of the Marquis of Hastings in the campaigns against the Mahrattas in 1816-1817. When peace was signed with the Maharajah Scindiah, Fitzclarence crossed India with despatches for England via Nagpor, the Ellora Caves and Bombay. He includes a view of the caves seen by the light of flaming torches and also gives images of some native military uniforms, among other interesting plates. The concensus in Abbey is that this volume is very scarce, the entire print run having been bought up by the author Fitzclarence himself. Fitzclarence became the first Earl of Munster in 1831. He was renowned as the President of the Royal Asiatic Society of London. He was the eldest son of the numerous children of the Duke of Clarence, later King William IV and his mistress Mrs. Jordan.

244

FORREST [Lieut-Colonel Charles Ramus].
A Picturesque Tour along the Rivers Ganges and Jumna in India.
London, R. Ackermann, 1824,

4to, title with handcoloured aquatint vignette on title, folding engraved map, 24 handcoloured aquatint plates by T. Sutherland and G. Hunt after Forrest, handcoloured aquatint vignette at end of text, this copy extra-illustrated with ORIGINAL WATERCOLOUR of the Palace of Delhi by Forrest, the view was taken from the principal mosque in Delhi, dated 28.4.1809, signed CRF No. 32 and laid down as a frontispiece, later half morocco, spine gilt in compartments.
Abbey Travel 441; Tooley 227; Prideaux, pp. 248; Martin Hardie, pp. 109-10; Colas 888; Lipperheide 1486.

Plates engraved by T. Sutherland, G. Hunt, after Forrest. Apart from the additional vignette on the title-page there is an unsigned aquatint vignette "Sicre Gully Pass, between Bengal and Bahar". The book was originally published in parts. A Prospectus of the book in a catalogue of Ackermann's for 1824 states: To be published in Six Monthly Numbers, price 14s. each... A few copies printed on Atlas 4to price 21s per Number. This was intended as a companion to Ackermann's Tours of the Rhine and Seine. An Italian edition was published containing a title-page, six pages of text and the plates as the English edition and a Spanish one in 1827.

245

FOTHERINGHAM, J.F.F.
Sporting Sketches and Scenes in India.
London, C. Moody, 1851.

First edition. Oblong 4to, 7 handcoloured lithographed plates, by and after Fotheringham, plate nos. 4-7 bear the name of the printer C. Moody, without lithographed title, but with accompanying text, original red publisher's cloth gilt. Schwerdt I, p.182c.

One of the few books dealing with the chase of the wild boar of the east, as the author calls it. Important for this particular sport, hoghunting or more commonly pigsticking in India.

246

FRANCIS, Charles Richard.
Sketches of Native Life in India with Views in Rajpootana, Simlah, etc. etc.
London, Meldola, Cahn & Co., sold by A. Hill, Princes Street, Edinburgh, copies of the work also from Grindlay & Co's…, London, 1848.

Small folio, 22 handcoloured lithographed plates, by J.C. Anderson after C.H. Fairland, subscription list at end, presentation copy from the author to Mrs Lewis Munro on title, original half leather, gilt ruled over green cloth, upper cover gilt lettered, g.e.

Not in usual bibliographies (a copy appeared in The Travis Sale, Sotheby's, Lot 124, 26th May 2004).

247

FRASER, James Baillie.
Journal of a Tour through Part of the Snowy Range of the Himala Mountains, and to the Sources of the Rivers Jumna and Ganges.
London, Rodwell and Martin, 1820.

First edition. 4to, engraved title, engraved folding map, published as the Act directs by Messrs Rodwell & Martin, contemporary polished calf, triple gilt fillets, spine gilt decorated. Abbey Travel 498 which mentions this 4to text with description of folio of plates below; Prideaux p. 336.

Abbey quotes from a Rodwell and Martin Catalogue, interesting because it shows the integration of publishing and bookselling at this time, and the degree of co-operation achieved in the publicising of such a work over the whole of Great Britain, despite the hazards of travel and communication: "The original drawings may be seen at the publishers, where the subscribers names are received. Specimens of the plates may be seen at the following booksellers, where Subscribers names are also received: J. and A. Arch, Cornhill; Black, Parbury, and Allen, Leadenhall Street, London; W. Blackwood, and Manners and Miller, Edinburgh; J. Cumming, and N. Mahon, Dublin. It is interesting, also, that Rodwell and Martin take the pains to say that the work is uniform with the Daniell (1795-1807), and the Salt (1809), neither of which folios was published by them. Obviously a display on the library table of the large illustrated topographical works on foreign travel, which had become so popular in the last twenty years or so was visualized as being an essential for every gentleman's library in Great Britain, whether its owner was diplomat, merchant, or squire. Many of these weighty folios are represented in this collection. Fraser's description of his travels was published also by Rodwell and Martin, as a 4to vol. in 1820, with an engraved map, selling for £3.3s on ordinary paper, or £4.4s. on large paper, presumably in boards.

This work serves as a companion volume to Fraser's Views in the Himala Mountain.

248

FRASER, James Baillie.
Views in the Himala Mountains.
London, Rodwell & Martin,1820-[c. 1827].

Folio, handcoloured aquatint title, and 20 finely handcoloured aquatint plates by R. Havell and Son after J.B. Fraser, contemporary red morocco gilt.
Abbey Travel 498; not in Tooley.

These magnificent plates have been described by Godrej & Rohatgi as "among the finest aquatints of mountain scenery ever produced" Fraser was the eldest son of a landed Scottish family, who followed several brothers to India and became a merchant in Calcutta in early 1814. Much of his spare time was spent sketching, painting and writing and he was a pupil of famous artist and teacher George Chinnery, of whom D'Oyly (see above in this catalogue) was also a pupil. Fraser visited the Himalayas in 1815 and 1816 and was encouraged on his return to Calcutta to have his drawings published.

249

FRASER, James Baillie.
Views of Calcutta, and its Environs, from Drawings
Executed…from Sketches made on the Spot.
London, Printed for Rodwell and Martin, 18[24]-1825-
[1826].

Folio, 24 handcoloured aquatint plates by R. Havell, F.C. Lewis
and Fielding after J.B. Fraser, each bearing the imprint of
Smith, Elder & Co. although plate 9 was published by Messrs
Rodwell & Martin, mid-nineteenth century half morocco gilt,
spine to a Romantic design and gilt in compartments, original
printed wrappers bound in.
Abbey Travel 494 (reference); not in Tooley; Archer p. 8;
Prideaux p. 336.

It will be noticed that the work was begun by Rodwell and
Martin, but was apparently completed and extended by
Smith, Elder. Rodwell and Martin, as is shown by the back
wrapper of Part I and by an 1824 catalogue of theirs,
intended to publish twelve plates only, in four parts. In fact
they seem to have given up, for some reason after taking a
year to publish Parts 1 to 3 and prepare one plate of Part 4
dated March 1st 1825. In just one year Smith Elder
published, in the space of six months, a further four parts,
containing 12 plates, bringing in F.C. Lewis and Fielding as
engravers in addition to Havell. At the same time they
evidently printed a new impression of all the plates,
altering the Rodwell and Martin imprints to Smith, Elder,
since most copies of the book seem to carry Smith, Elder
(undated) imprints throughout.

Portico of a Hindoo Temple,

with other Hindoo and Mahometan Buildings,

from sketches by Capt. Grindlay.

Published by Smith, Elder & Co. Cornhill, London.

GOLD, Capt. Charles.

Oriental Drawings: sketched between the Years 1791 and 1798.

London, Bunney and Co., for G. and W. Nicoll, 1806.

First edition. 4to, 48 handcoloured aquatint plates, one vignette, the exception is plate 23, an engraved plate of musical instruments, and this a coloured line engraving, an uncoloured aquatint of a Hindoo Fakir appears on the verso of leaf 38 of text, later portrait of Gold in watercolour by his three times Great Grandson together with a family tree as a frontispiece, later half morocco over pebbled cloth, spine raised bands, label gilt lettered, m.e.

Abbey Travel 428; not in Tooley; Archer pp. 72, 79-80; Cox Vol. I, p. 310; Martin Hardie, p. 134; Prideaux, pp. 247, 338.

An interesting and individual choice of subjects of life, custom and costume, including a female Brahmin and a Gentoo woman, an artillery elephant, sepoys, snake-men, juggler, barbarous ceremony, smoking the hooka, Mysorean cavalry etc. Later plates signed, engraved by Medland and Wells, earlier plates drawn from life or nature by C. Gold.

GRINDLAY, Capt. Robert Melville.

Scenery, Costumes and Architecture... of India.

London, R. Ackermann [Smith Elder & Co.], 1826-[1830].

2 vols. in one, folio, introduction, text Part I, 6 leaves, text in Part II, 7 leaves, engraved title with handcoloured vignette to Vol. I, 36 handcoloured aquatint plates, no. 20 an uncoloured lithograph, two advertisement leaves at end, Vol. II with lithographed vignette title, contemporary straight grained red morocco elaborate gilt filleting and blindstamped borders with gilt cornerpieces, central panels, entirely covered with interlaced blindstamping, spine raised bands gilt ruled and lettered, narrow inner gilt dentelles, g.e.

Abbey Travel 442; Archer, p. 7; colas 1333; Martin Hardie pp. 94, 115, 149, 314; Prideaux p. 121, 248-9, 338, 376; Sutton No. 71 (p. 184) is plate no. 19; Tooley (1954) No. 239.

As can be seen from the title-pages and from the plate imprints the work was begun by Ackermann, but was taken over and completed by Smith, Elder & Co. Sams in fact joined Ackermann for the second part of Vol. I. It is possible that Ackermann was finding insufficient support for the book. However, if this is so his gloom seems unjustified as Smith Elder's reprints show, and the book is still relatively common (Abbey). The use of lithography for the title in Vol. II of this aquatint work by Smith Elder is interesting as a sign of the growing reputation of the newer medium, which , within approximately ten years was to supersede the more skilled expensive art of aquatinting. An earlier and more ambitious attempt to use lithography instead of aquatint, an attempt evidently before its time, is discussed in the Notes to Lycett's Views in Australia, 1824, No. 571. "A beautiful and splendid work. – Just look at the frontispiece..." This was from Blackwood's Magazine, in a colloquy between Christopher North (John Wilson) and the Shepherd (James Hogg) on one of the Noctes Ambrosianae. North rhapsodizes over the plates, impressing the shepherd with his knowledge of India, "I have been assured by quoting the Captain, who writes as well as he draws. Pen, pencil, or sword, come alike to the hand of an accomplished British officer." All considerable and good publicity for the work from this literary magazine.

HARDINGE, The Hon. Charles Stewart.

Recollections of India. Drawn on stone by J.D. Harding from the Original Drawings by...Charles Stewart Hardinge. Part I: British India and the Punjab; Part II: Kashmir and the Alpine Punjab.
London, Thomas M'Lean, 1847.

First edition. 2 parts in one vol., folio, 26 handcoloured tinted lithographed plates, all mounted on card, on guards in original publisher's green cloth with half morocco gilt ruled, g.e.
Abbey Travel 472; Tooley (1954) 244.

Hardinge became the second Viscount in 1856. Hardinge himself was no mean painter in water-colours. In 1847 his friends in England published a folio volume entitled Recollections of India, consisting of twenty lithographs from his drawings made in India. The most interesting of these are portraits of Sikh chieftains and views of scenery in Kashmir, then an almost unknown country, which he visited in company with John Nicholson, afterwards the hero of Delhi.

HARRIS, Captain Claudius [and] GUIAND, J.
Ruins of Mandoo.
London, Day & Son, 1860.

Folio, title, subscription leaf, preface, list of plates, text pp. 1-20, imprint of Day & Son, 6 tinted lithographed plates, handcoloured, original grey-blue moiré cloth lettered in gilt on upper cover, blindstamped direct, preserved in green cloth box. Abbey Travel 490.

Plates include the modern village of Mandoo and of the ancient Mosque, the Jumah Musjid; the Palace of Sultan Baz Bahadoor, and Pavilion of Roop Muttee, his Queen; the Jahaz Mahal, or Water Palace.

HART, Captain Lockyer Willis.
Character and Costumes in Afghaunistan.
[London, Henry Graves and Company,1843].

First edition. Large folio, handcoloured engraved map,
lithographed pictorial title and 26 handcoloured lithographed
plates, letterpress description of the plates mounted on card,
the whole loose in original morocco backed folder gilt, label
on upper cover.
Abbey Travel 511.

The rare portfolio issue, with the plates handcoloured and
mounted on card.

Hart was a Captain in the 22nd Regiment Bombay
Infantry. The plates show scenes of everyday life in Kabul,
for instance one of a kebab stand, as well as portraits of
Emir Dost Mohammed and other dignitaries.

255

255

HODGES, William.
Select Views in India, Drawn on the Spot, in the Years 1780, 1781, 1782, and 1783.
London, J. Edwards, [1785-86].

Folio, title and text in English and French, engraved map of part of the rivers Ganges, Mumna, Goomty and Gogra, 48 handcloured aquatint plates, full red morocco elaborately gilt, tooled by Kalthoeber.
Abbey Travel 415; Tooley 264.

This work was compiled from a series of drawings by Hodges executed during a stay in India as a guest of Warren Hastings from 1780-83. Hodges arrived in India at Madras, then explored the Coromandel coast and went on to visit Calcutta, Bengal, Patna, Benares and Bidjegur before returning to Calcutta due to illness. On his recovery he then travelled to Allahabad, Cawnpoor, Lucknow, Fyzabad, Agra and Fatehpur Sikri and back to Calcutta. Hodges had served as draughtsman to Captain Cook on his second voyage (1772-1775), sailing round the world and supervising engravings of the illustrations for the official account of the voyage. Hodge's work, much more romantic than later sets of views of India, was nonetheless very popular and in fact encouraged Thomas Daniell to master the art of aquatinting to emulate Hodge's commercial success.

HOME, Robert.
[A Description of Seringapatam].
London, R. Bowyer, 1796.

Oblong folio, 6 handcoloured aquatint plates on card, by Stadler after Home, plate titles within grey wash borders, loose as issued in modern cloth folder, ties, label on upper cover.
Not in Abbey; Prideaux; Hardie; Franklin or Tooley.

A very rare and beautiful series of aquatint plates. Home, at one time a pupil of Angelica Kauffmann, travelled to Lucknow and for many years was the chief painter to the King of Oude. He amassed a considerable fortune with his ceremonial paintings. In 1797 he sent home a painting to the R.A. of the "Reception of Mysore Princes as Hostages by Marquis Cornwallis". A painting of his of "Shah Zumeen, King of Oude, Receiving Tribute", presented by a relation in 1828 hangs in Hampton Court, and he also painted an official of Marquis Wellesley, among other notables. While in India, Home made numerous topographical drawings, scenes of the campaign, 29 of them published in his Select Views in Mysore.

IRWIN, Lieut. J.F.
Views in Southern Afghanistan.
London, Smith Elder, Standidge & Co., Vincent Brooks, Day & Son, [1870].

Small folio, 8 coloured lithographed plates, by Bedford after Irwin, loose and without title or text, in original cloth gilt folder, lettered direct, ties.
Not in Abbey or Tooley.

With news clipping of map of Cabul, Daily Telegraph, December 20, 1879.

JACK, [Lieut. Col. Alexander].
Six Views of Kot Kangra and the surrounding Country.
London, Smith, Elder & Co., 1847.

First edition. Large folio, tinted lithographed pictorial title, letterpress dedication and leaf of descriptive text, 6 handcoloured lithographed plates by G. Childs, J. Picken, T.S. Boys and W. Walton after Jack, some heightened with gum Arabic, loose as issued, in modern morocco backed boards, morocco labelling piece gilt on upper cover.
Abbey Travel 473; not in Tooley.

Alexander Jack of the Bengal Infantry, was present at the battle of Aliwal and acted as Brigadier of the force sent against the fort at Kangra in the Punjab. He was commended for bringing up his 18-pounder guns which he had been advised to leave behind. The march was said "to reflect everlasting credit on the Bengal artillery" (DNB). He was to die during the Cawnpore Mutiny with most of his men.

259

JACKSON, Sir Keith A.
Views in Affghaunistan.
London. W.H. Allen & Co., [1841].

First edition. 4to, handcoloured lithographed frontispiece, tinted lithographed pictorial title with handcoloured vignette, lithographed dedication, 25 handcoloured tinted lithographed plates all mounted on card, lacking map-Route of the Army of the Indus, 17 ll. text, modern wrappers, preserved in large folio morocco backed cloth folder gilt.
Abbey Travel 506.

Travis quotes a copy with 25 plates albeit with the route map, as being a complete copy, which they describe as rare. So it would seem that this plate count of 25 would also be the complete complement of coloured plates. Plates of views in and around Cabul and also towards Jellabad.

PORTRAIT. OF AN AFFGHAUN.

Fac-Simile of a Drawing in colours found in the women's Anderoon at Ghuznee on July 23rd 1839, just after the storming of that Fortress; supposed to be the Portrait of an Affghaun Exquisite.

259

260

JAMES, Captain.
The Military Costume of India in an Exemplifaction of the Manual and Platoon Excercises Used for the Use of the Native Troops and the British Army in General.
London, T. Goddard of the Military Library, 1814.

Small folio, engraved and colour printed title, 34 engraved and colour printed plates, all by Sawyer, 8 pp. preface, 34 pp. text, no. 2-35, large paper copy, contemporary half red straight grained morocco.
Colas 1536; Ogilby Trust Index to British Military Costume Prints 1500-1914; not in Lipperheide; Brunet III, 495; Vinet 2352.

There are copies which bear the date of 1813 on title, but which are otherwise identical. Colas also identifies large paper copies as here.

261

JUMP, R. Capt.
Views in Calcutta.
London, Parbury & Co., 1837.

Oblong 4to, 6 handcoloured lithographed plates of Calcutta, each mounted and loose, preserved in a modern green cloth covered box.
Abbey Travel 496.

The descriptive text of the plates was printed inside front and back wrappers. The plates were signed On Stone by Capt. R. Jump, except for No. 1 and Printed by Standidge & Co., London. They comprise the Kidderpore Bridge which was lithographed by P. Gauci; Bahleah Ghaut; Burra Bazaar; the Martiniere; Roop Chund Roy Street; Government House.

LYTTLETON, Lieut.
A Set of Views in the Island of Ceylon.
London, Edward Orme, 1819.

Folio, engraved title with dedication, 6 handcoloured aquatint plates engraved by Dubourg after the author, each caption is headed: Ceylon View No.1 [6], labels carrying descriptive text are tipped on to the left margin of each subject, these vary in size with the amount of text, later half green morocco over labelled boards, gilt ruled, label gilt on upper cover.
Abbey Travel 411; not in de Silva.

Plates include views of Amanapoora, on the Road from Columbo to Kandy; the Summit of the Balani Mount; the King's Palace at Kandy; the Ferry at Wattepalogoa, three miles from Kandy; Tombs of Kandyan Kings at the North end of the Town of Kandy; Town of Kandy, from Castle Hill. An attractive and apparently scarce set.

263

McCURDY, Captain E.A.
Three Panoramic Views of Ottacamund, the chief station
on the Neilgherries, or Blue Mountains of Coimbetore,
showing the situation of all the houses at that
Sanatorium of the South of India.
London, Smith Elder & Co., [c. 1830].

First edition. Large oblong folio, three coloured lithographed
views each on one sheet by W.L. Walton after McCurdy, plus
vignette title, original wrappers lithographed with vignette,
spine recently strengthened and preserved in morocco backed
linen cover box, a scarce work.
Not in Abbey.

Scarce. This area of the Punjab, Southern India was rarely
illustrated.

264

MECHAM, Lieut. Clifford Henry.
Sketches and Incidents of the Siege of Lucknow.
London, Day & Son, 1858.

First edition. Folio, tinted lithographed pictorial title and 26
lithographed views with some handcolouring on 17 sheets,
8pp., accompanying text, original brown cloth decorated in gilt.
Not in usual bibliographies.

Eye-witness report of the siege of Lucknow, describing
anddepicting the heavy toll suffered by the British.

Nº. 26. LYING IN WAIT.

Nº 27. SINKING A SHAFT.

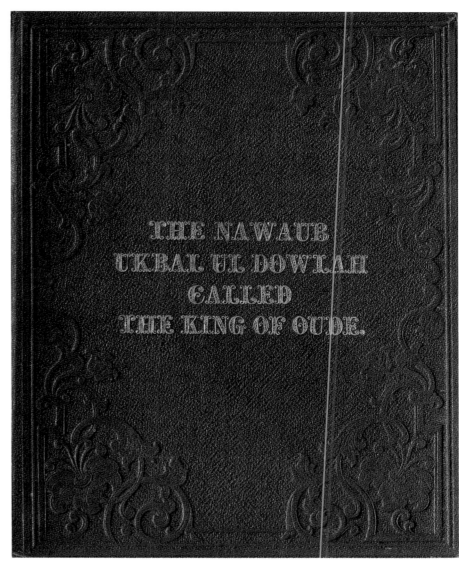

265

[OUDHE], H.J.
The Nawab Ukbal ul Dowlah called the King of Oudhe.
The King of Oudhe, his Brother and Attendants. Sketched
while on a visit to England.
London, Ackermann & Co., n.d., [c. 1825].

Small 8vo, 8 handcoloured lithographed plates (each signed
"HJ"), original blindstamped red cloth, gilt lettered on upper cover.
Not in Lipperheide, Colas or Abbey.

An apparently scarce work.

266

[PUNJAUB.]
Original Sketches in the Punjaub by a Lady.
London, Dickinson Brothers, 1854.

First edition. Oblong folio, title, preface, double column, 1 leaf,
verso with text to Plate 1, one leaf of text to each subsequent
plate, rectos blank, 20 handcoloured lithographed plates,
unsigned, original red cloth blindstamped & gilt.
Abbey Travel 483.

A rare work. One of the very few early British books to
illustrate Lahore, Amritsar and the Sikh Holy Places.
"Possibly privately published" (Abbey).

267

RATTRAY, James.
The Costumes of the Various tribes, Portraits of Ladies of Rank, celebrated Princes and chiefs, Views of the Principal Fortresses and cities, and Interior of the Cities and Temples of Afghaunistan.
London, Hering and Remington, 1848.

First edition. Large folio, title printed in red and black, handcoloured lithographed additional pictorial title and 29 handcoloured plates on 25 sheets after Rattray, many heightened with gum Arabic, tissue guards, list of subscribers, errata leaf tipped in (8vo), publisher's advertisement leaf, original publisher's half red morocco gilt.
Abbey Travel 513; Colas 2489; Lipperheide 1479.

Rattray's work is set against the background of the first Afghan War in 1838 by which a British force replaced the Emir Dost Mohammed with the pro-British Shah Suja as part of a policy designed to contain Russian expansion. The subscription list suggests that the work was planned before the confusion of 1841-42 and includes Sir Alexander Burnes and Sir William Macnaughten, both killed at Kabul in 1841. The work is dedicated to the Kandahar force and its late General William Nott, under whom Rattray served. The work includes some beautiful plates and native portraits. Views include Kandahar, Kabul and Lugdulluk, the scene of the annihilation of Elphinstone's force. Strangely in the face of such tragedy the overall impression is upbeat, showing the Afghan people as attractive and perhaps exotic.

SALE, Major General Sir Robert Henry.
The Defence of Jellalabad…drawn on stone by W.L. Walton.
[London, J. Hogarth and H. Graves, [c. 1845].

Folio, lithographed portrait of Sale on India proof paper, pictorial lithographed title on thick grey paper, dedication and 22 handcoloured lithographed plates on 11 mounts, lithographed double-page plan of Jellalabad, 5pp. text, contemporary half green straight grained morocco over cloth. Not in Abbey.

The retreat to Jellalabad had been one of the most devastating retreats in the history of the British army in Afghanistan and of the 10th Somerset Regiment. Of those who left Kabul to join Sale in Jellabad, only one hundred survived to be taken prisoner, and one man alone arrived at Jellabad.

269

269

SIMPSON, William [and] KAYE, Sir John William.
India Ancient and Modern. A Series of Illustrations of the
Country and People of India and adjacent Territories.
London, Day and Son, 1867.

First edition. 2 vols., folio, 50 chromolithographed plates, text
with title printed in black and red, chromolithographed
dedication, the plates are listed in the text vol., half burgundy
morocco over marbled boards.
Not in Abbey; not in BL (Rare).

The text includes the Lanka caves of Ellora; Cashmere shawl
manufactory; the Chitpore Road, a street in Bombay,
Bombay's girls school; Cave of Elephanta; Indian woman,
floating lamps on the Gangees; Native shop in a Calcutta
bazaar; the Khyber Pass; the Goveror General's State Howdar;
the Falls of Gairsoppa; The Dewali, or feast of lamps.

270

SOLVYNS, B[altazar].
The Costume of Indostan, elucidated by Sixty Coloured
Engravings; with Descriptons in English and French,
taken in the Years 1798 and 1799.
London, W. Bulmer & Co., Sold & Published by Edwd

Orme, 1804-5.

Small folio, title and text and dedication in English and French,
60 engraved, handcoloured plates, each accompanied by leaf
of explanatory text, English recto, French verso, full black calf gilt.
Tooley 461; Abbey Travel 429 cites 1807 edition; Colas 2765;
Brunet V, 433.

William Orme made water-colour copies from Solvyns's
originals, for the engravers. These copies are much better
drawn than Solvyns's originals, and the above stipple
engravings are correspondingly an improvement on
Solvyns's etchings. Both Solvyns's originals and Orme's
copies are now in the Victoria and Albert Museum. Solvyns
himself published an improvement on his original work,
in Paris, 1808-12, four volumes, containing 288 plates
(see next item).

Abbey's opinion of the merits of the various editions is
based on comparison with London handcoloured plate
books of this period. In fact these plates, whilst beautiful,
have lost something of the character of the original
Calcutta plates etched on handmade paper by Solvyns
himself. Those were perhaps slightly idiosyncratic, but
more alive and true to nature than these rather more
formalised plates.

SOLVYNS, Baltazar.

Les Hindous ou la Description de leurs Moeurs Coutumes et Ceremonies.

Paris, Chez l'Auteur, de l'Imprimerie de Mame Freres, 1808-1812.

Large folio, 4 vols., originally issued in 48 parts, 288 engraved handcoloured plates, some double-page, plus four engraved titles, contemporary green half straight grained morocco over marbled boards, uncut.

Brunet V, 432; Colas 2767.

The images are lively and well executed, showing costumes and customs of the Hindous. A very rare edition with very few copies still existing. Solvyns an ex sea captain from Belgium, immersed himself in the Hindu way of life. The plates show a fidelity and honesty which is rarely found in portrayals of foreigners by Europeans at this time. Facial expressions, attitudes of figures, their costumes and occupations are shown with incredible accuracy. This work was used as a source for many other works on the Hindus. Made up of the following sections: Hindoo Castes and Respective Professions; Section II. Servants; Section III Dresses of Hindoo Men; Section IV. Dresses of Hindoo women. V. Vehicles, Horses and Bullocks VI. Palanquins VII. Faquirs Section VIII. Pleasure Boats; Section IX. Boats; Section X. Various Modes of Smoking with the Hooka etc. Section XI. Musical Instruments. Section XII. Public Festivals, Funerals, Ceremonies etc. This work in its original form appeared etched by Solvyns in Calcutta, on handmade paper.

TAYLER, William.
Sketches illustrating the Manners and Customs of the Indians and Anglo-Indians, drawn on stone from the original drawings from life.
London, Thomas M'Lean, 1842.

First edition. Folio, lithographed title and 6 handcoloured lithographed plates by J. Bouvier after Tayler, contemporary morocco backed watered cloth over boards, gilt lettered direct on upper cover.
Colas 2858; Abbey Travel 465.

Plates 1-3 are headed Anglo Indians, plates 4-6 are headed Indians. The first three relate to household scenes of toilet and breakfast.

TAYLOR, Lieut. Col.
Letters on India, Political, Commercial and Military, relative to Subjects important to the British Interests in the East. Addressed to a Proprietor of East-India Stock.
London, S. Hamilton, 1800.

First edition. 4to, title, dedication, advertisement, preface ix-xxviii, text pp. 1-270, folding panorama of the Town, Fort, and Harbour of Bombay, taken from the Malabar Hill, handcoloured aquatint by T. Ran [cropped], for Lieut. Col. Taylor's work, folding map, two charts, of which one is folding, contemporary sprinkled calf, double gilt fillet, spine gilt in compartments, raised bands, edges sprinkled.
Abbey Travel 423.

The engraver is something of a mystery, as no engraver is listed in Prideaux or Thieme und Becker whose name begins T. Ran... There is a second panorama of Bombay Harbour in this collection, preserved loose in a modern red morocco backed box by Wates.

DRAWN BY W. TAYLER ESQᴿ BENGAL CIVIL SERVICE.

LITHO. BY J. BOUVIER.

THE YOUNG CIVILIANS TOILET.

Published Feby. 1st. 1842, for the Proprietor by T. McLean 26. Haymarket.

PRINTED AT THE GENᴸ LITHᵍ ESTABᵗ 70 Sᵗ MARTINS LANE.

TEMPLE, Lieut. Richard.
Eight Views of the Mauritius Comprising the Position of the British Army, commanded by the Honble. Genl. J. Abercrombie, on the 29th & 30th. Of Novr. & 1st. of Decr. 1810, also of the town and harbour of Port Louis. [London, published by W. Haines, n.d., n.p., imprints dated 1813, plates watermarked 1811.]

First edition. Oblong folio, engraved throughout, title, 8 handcoloured aquatint plates by J. Clark after Temple, later half red morocco over green boards.
Abbey Travel I, 293 (a late issue with 1830 watermarks); Tooley 481; Prideaux, p. 353.

This work gives a very good visual record of the scenery of the island and the military and naval operation which led to the British seizing the island from the French.
General Sir John Abercromby (1772-1817) landed on 29 November 1810 with a force of over 11,000 men, and after a smart action which showed the French general that resistance was impossible…on 2 Dec. Decaen surrendered the island" (DNB)
  Tooley dates the book 1810 and Tooley 1811. However, 1810 is clearly that of the operations and 1811 that of the dedication. The other set of Temple's drawings by Hayne relating to a Naval campaign in the Persian Gulf, see under Africa in the catalogue, are in a very similar style and were published in the same year.

WILLIAMS, Capt. John.
An Historical Account of the Rise and Progress of the Bengal Native Infantry from its first Formation in 1757 to 1796.
London, John Murray, C. Rowath, 1817.

8vo, title with imprint, 4 handcoloured stipple engravings with some aquatinting, contemporary blue and brown paper over boards.
Not in Colas; Lipperheide 2266; Abbey Travel 439; Martin Hardie p. 134; Prideaux p. 357 (given in error under Captain Williamson).

There was evidently a second edition of this which appeared in 1819. The plates show Subadar; Grenadier Sepoy; Hawuldar; and Light Infantry Sepoy.

**WILLIAMSON, Capt. Thomas and
HOWETT, Samuel.**
Oriental Field Sports; being a complete, detailed and
accurate description of the Wild Sports of the East.
London, Thomas M'Lean, 1807.

Oblong folio, 40 handcoloured aquatint plates after
Williamson and Howett, plate list in English and French,
nineteenth century brown half morocco, upper cover with the
original colour printed engraved pictorial frontispiece trimmed
and laid down.
Abbey Travel 427 (edition of 1807); Schwerdt II, p. 298 (1807
& 1808); Archer p. 7; Martin Hardie pp. 135-6, 302-3;
Prideaux 281-3, 357.

"The most beautiful book on Indian sport in existence"
(Schwerdt). In 1805 Orme produced a two vol. 8vo
edition with B. Crosby and this edition is in Schwerdt. In
this remarkable work, Abbey singularises the frontispiece
which shows a tiger reclining on a rock. He regards the
printing process as remarkable, giving a brilliant effect in
oil colour. The process may have been a stencil, one similar
to modern silk screen.

²⁷⁷
WOOD, William, Jnr.
A Series of Twenty-Eight Panoramic Views of Calcutta,
extending from Chandpaul Ghaut to the end of
Chowringhee Road, together with the Hospital, the two
Bridges, and the Fort.
London, Parbury, Allen, & Co., Rodwell, W. Wood,
Engelmann & Co. lithog. [1833].

Folio, 28 handcoloured lithographed plates, without text as
issued, plates apart from No. 16 numbered Pl.1 [27],
lithographed by W.Wood Junr., Engelmann & Co., C.
Hullmandel, Graf & Soret, Graf & Coindet, half brown
morocco stamped in blind over marbled boards.
Abbey Travel 495.

83 sets of the work were subscribed in India and 38 in
England. Bohn stated that the work was originally produced
in 6 parts, and if this is the case the Part 6 wrapper is
missing in the Abbey copy. Since the plates were loose the
number of plates given in each part is not necessarily of any
significance. ABPC described one copy of the book as
having 40 plates, but 40 may be a mistake. It seems most
unlikely that Wood ever did more than 28 plates. Wood was
probably the son of William Wood, 1774-1857, the
zoologist, surgeon, artist, and bookseller.

East Indies and Far East

AA, Cornelis van der.
Atlas van der Zeehavens der Batafsche Republiek.
Mitsgaders de Afbeeldingen van de Haring Visscherij en
de Walvisch Vangst.
Amsterdam, E. Maaskamp, 1805.

First edition, Folio, half title, engraved title, 31 doublepage
plates, without text, contemporary vellum backed blue paper
boards.

Very rare. Fine engravings of whale and herring fishing.
The only copy of this Atlas to appear at auction was at
Sotheby's in May 2004. A facsimile edition appeared at
Beijers in 1976.

279

BARROW, Sir John.
Travels in China containing descriptions, observations,
and comparisons, made and collected in the course of a
short residence at the Imperial Palace of Yuen-Min-
Yuen, and on a subsequent journey through the country
from Pekin to Canton. In which it is attempted to
appreciate the rank that this extraordinary Empire may
be considered to hold in the scale of civilized nations.
London, T. Cadell & W. Davies, 1804.

First edition. 4to, 11 handcoloured aquatint views on 8 plates,
some after W. Alexander and one after S. Daniell, engraved by
T. Medland, plates 5, 6 and 7 coloured aquatints, No. 1 is
coloured aquatint and stipple, No. 3 coloured stipple and Nos.
5, 6 and 7, uncoloured line engravings, contemporary mottled
calf.
Tooley 84; Lust 365; Abbey Travel 531; Cox I, 346; Cordier
cols. 2388-9; Prideaux p. 249, 327; Sutton No. 57 (p. 181) is
No. 3 above.

A second edition was published in 1806 at the same price.
This second edition was remaindered by Bohn, 1847,
together with the second edition of Barrow's Travels into
the Interior of Southern Africa and again the second
edition (although not specified) of a Voyage to
Cochinchina, 1807 as a four volume set. Barrow like
William Alexander was in the suite of Lord Macartney's
Embassy of 1792 to the Emperor of China. The expedition
provided the material for a number of interesting works
on China, of which the above book, and Alexander's
Costume of China, 1805 are notable examples. Lord
Amherst's embassy of 1816 was also accompanied by a
draughtsman who was to make a name for himself,
William Havell, but only five plates after drawings of his
appeared in any work on China, as is discussed in the
Notes to Henry Ellis's book.

280

BARROW, Sir John.
A Voyage to Cochinchina, in the Years 1792 and 1793;
containing General View of the Valuable Productions and
the Political Importance of this Flourishing Kingdom;
and also of such European Settlements as were visited on
the Voyage…
London, T. Cadell & W. Davies, 1806.

First edition. 4to, two folding maps, double-page coloured
plan of the Town and Harbour of Rio de Janeiro and a double
page chart of the Southern Extremity of Africa, handcoloured in
outline, 19 handcoloured aquatint plates, the first two drawn
by S. Daniell, others drawn by W. Alexander, the last three
plates drawn by Alexander after sketches by S. Daniell.
Abbey Travel 514; Cordier 2424; Borba de Moraes, p. 88;
Mendelssohn I, p. 43.

280

Gordon-Brown p. 83. Barrow probably met Samuel Daniell
while at the Cape, when Daniell was working on his African
Scenery and Animals, 1804-5. The aquatinting in this work
is of excellent quality, No. 10 in particular being technically
interesting, since it appears to be printed in as many as
three colours, with one colour added by hand, while No. 11
is printed in green, with other colours added by hand.

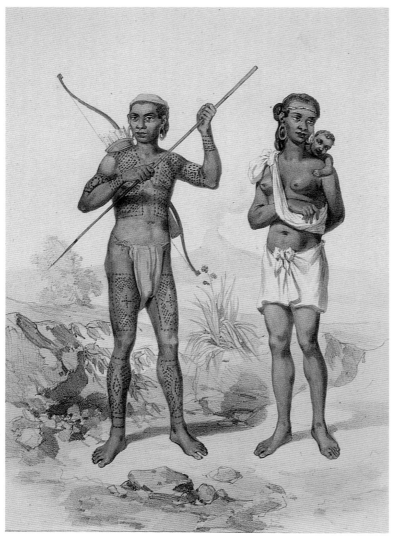

281

281

281

BASSILAN, Jean-Baptiste Mallat de.
Les Philippines histoire, geographie, moeurs, agriculture, industrie et commerce…Atlas.
Paris, Arthus Bertrand, [1836].

Atlas vol. only, folio, folding map handcoloured in outline, 10 handcoloured plates, 7 other maps or plans on 4 leaves and one folding leaf of music, contemporary half calf.
Not in Colas or Lipperheide; Robertson p.134.

An unusual series of illustrations of the Philippines including genre scenes, everyday life, including agriculture, industry and commerce.
   "A work of considerable merit… the atlas accompanying the work is very rare and we have not seen it" (Robertson).

282

BOCK, Carl.
Head-Hunters of Borneo; a Narrative of Travel up the Mahakkam and down the Barito; also, Journeyings in Sumatra.
London, Sampson Low, Marston, Searle, and Rivington, 1881.

First English edition. Tall 8vo, 30 lithographed plates, mostly coloured, modern cloth.

Apparently scarce, not in usual bibliographies, although a first and second edition appeared in the recent Travis sale. The first edition was published in The Hague by Martinus Nijhoff also in 1881.

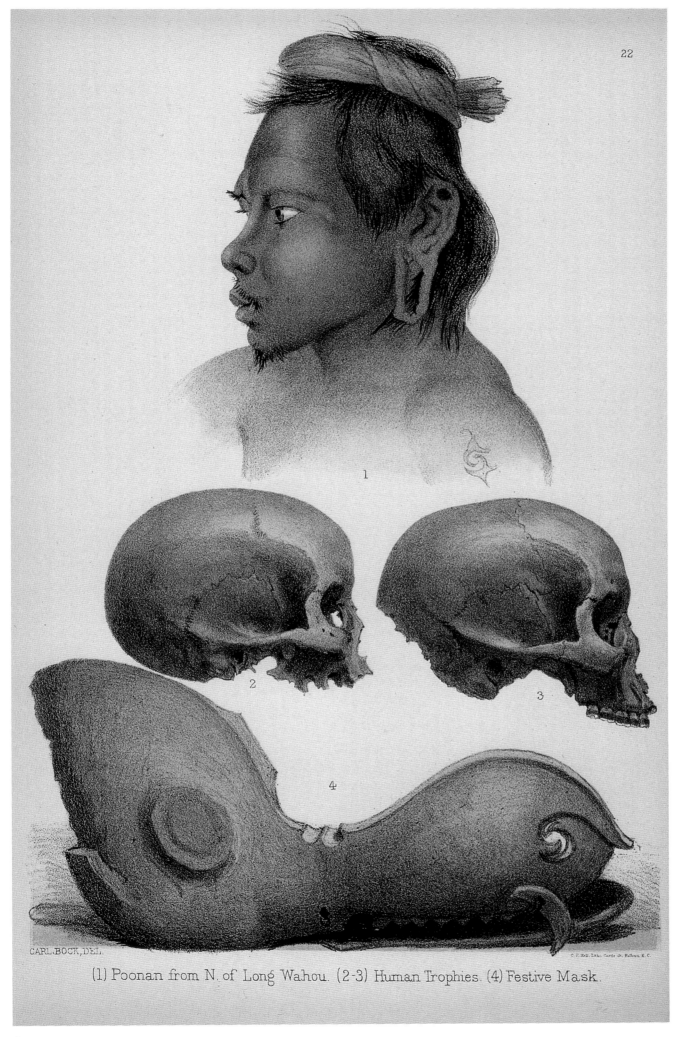

CARL BOCK, DEL.

C. F. Kell, Lithr, Castle St, Holborn, E.C.

(1) Poonan from N. of Long Wahou. (2-3) Human Trophies. (4) Festive Mask.

283

283

BORGET, Auguste [and] CICERI, Eugene.
La Chine et les Chinois, dessins executes d'apres Nature.
Paris, Chez Goupil & Vibert, 1842.

Large folio, pictorial lithographed title, dedication leaves to
Louis Philippe, 32 views on 25 sepia lithographs by Ciceri after
Borget, preliminaries and descriptive text, contemporary half
morocco over original cloth.
Brunet I, 1113; Cordier, Bibliotheca Sinica, 79-80.

An early view of Hong Kong, as well as of Macao and
Canton, showing scenery and scenes from Chinese life.

DANIELL, Thomas and William.
A Picturesque Voyage to India by the Way of China.
London, T. Davison, for Longman, Hurst, Rees and Orme,
and William Daniell, 1810.

First edition. Small folio, 50 handcoloured aquatint plates, half
red morocco.
Abbey Travel 516; Cordier II, 2107; Tooley (1954) 173.

This work describes and illustrates the Daniells' long
voyage to China and then on to India, beginning in April

1785 and ending in August of the same year. After several
months in China, they sailed on to Calcutta. This work is
particularly good for plates of Indonesia (Java and Malaya)
and of China itself (Macao, Canton River and Canton)
ending with views of the Bay of Bengal and Calcutta. The
accompanying text includes observations and descriptions
of the people and places visited.

DAVIS, John Francis.
La China illustrata e dipinta ossia descrizione generale
degli usi, de costumi, del governo...
Venice, Fratelli Battei, 1842.

2 vols. in one, large 8vo, 37 handcoloured plates,
2 handcoloured lithographed frontispieces, original boards.
Cordier Sinica, 73; cf Colas 808 & 809 which cite uncoloured
English and French editions.

Davis whose work was published in London in 1836 and
translated also into French in the following year was giving a
general description of the Empire of China and its inhabitants,
including religion, science, literature, arts, manufactures and
commerce. Davis had been His Majesty's Chief
Superintendant in China, described in the French edition as
the former President of the East India Company in China.

HARDOUIN E. [and] RITTER, Wilhelm Leonard.
Java Tooneelen uit het Levin Karakterschetsen en Kleederdragten van Java' Bewoners.
The Hague, Konrad Fuhri, 1855.

First edition. 4to, half title, title-page, second title page, contents 2pp., index 4pp; forward, by H.M. Lange, 6pp., 26 tinted lithographed plates, finished by hand and signed E. Hardouin Batavia, printed by Lemercier, Paris, folding map, contemporary calf backed boards.
Landwehr 301 (1853-1855 ed); Colas 1378 (1872 ed.); Lipperheide 1507 (1872).

The plates by Hardouin show Javanese costumes and genre scenes. Hardouin, born in France, was probably trained as a painter and draughtsman. He arrived in Batavia in 1842 as a décor designer with a French theatrical troupe in charge of F. Minard. In this capacity the Javasche Courant praised him for restoring the old decors in a "highly artful manner." In 1846 Hardouin applied and was granted permission to travel in central Java in connection with his interest in art and painting. Some of the plates in this work suggest he may have travelled in West Java and the Priangan and possibly in South Sumatra also (Bastin & Brommer).

291

HEINE, WILLIAM
Graphic Scenes of the Japan Expedition.
New York, G.P. Putnam and Co., 1856.

First edition. Folio, title, introduction leaf, and 10 handcoloured lithographed plates printed in colours, modern half maroon morocco.
Bennett, p. 53; McGrath, American Color Plate Books 123.

Heine was the official artist seconded to Commodore Perry's expedition to Japan (see above). He independently published this far more lavish set of plates. "The plates are beautiful Japanese scenes and places of special interest, many times finer than the plates in the 3 vol. Account of the Perry Expedition" (Bennett). Possibly this denigrates the Perry plates unfairly. They show interesting scenes from the expedition and some fine, though perhaps small, portraits after photographs, early use of this process, all lithographed.

292

HELMAN, Isadore Stanislas Henri.
Suite des Seizes Estampes Representant les Conquetes de l'Empereur de la Chine.
[Paris, Chez l'auteur, 1788].

Oblong folio, 24 engraved plates, plates XVIII, XIX, XX forming a panorama "Marche ordinaire de l'Empereur de la Chine l'orsqu'il passé dans la Ville de Peking," original grey boards.
Not in Cordier; Cohen de Ricci, 479.

293

HELMAN, Isadore Stanislas Henri.
Faits Memorables des Empereurs de la Chine Tires des Annales Chinoises.
Paris, Chez l'Auteur, [1788].

Oblong folio, 24 engraved plates, accompanied by a single engraved sheet of text, original grey paper over boards.
Cordier 587.

294

HELMAN, Isadore Stanislas Henri.
Abrege Historique des Principaux Traits de la Vie de Confucius Celebre Philosophe Chinois.
Paris, Chez l'auteur, [1788].

Oblong folio, engraved title, 24 engraved plates, two engraved double-sided leaves of text, original grey boards.
Cordier Biblioteca Sinica 667; P. Amiot's biography of Confucius, was the most important up to its date of publication, although it was not the first (Cordier).

The plates in these three albums were reductions of large engraved plates commissioned by the Jesuits in Paris for the Chinese Emperor showing his victories in a specific campaign.

295

JUNGHUHN, Franz Wilhelm.
Landschafts Ansichten von Java.
Leipzig, 1856-1857.

Oblong folio and 8vo, 3 vols. of text in 8vo, folder of 11 coloured lithographed plates in folio, plus cover, half red cloth, wih colour lithographed plate laid down on upper cover, (making a total of 12 plates).
Muller Junghuhn Bibliographie, p. 336; Bastin-Brommer, p. 29 and N473; Engelmann I, p. 136.

Rare early views of Java. "Franz Wilhelm Junghuhn was one of the first to visualize the immense splendour of Indonesian nature. He was born in Germany, where he studied medicine and natural sciences. He came to Indonesia in 1835 and became a medical officer in the Netherlands Indies Army. In 1839 he was transferred to Sumatra and a few years later became a member of the Natural Sciences Commission and became known for his importance as a scientist, author, draughtsman, philosopher and photographer. These views were first published in his "Java, seine Gestalt"… Leipzig, 1853. The plates according to Junghuhn were carefully chosen because they depicted typical Javanese landscapes.

296

[KINLOCH, Charles Walker.]

De Zieke Reiziger, or, Rambles in Java and the Straits in 1852 by a Bengal Civilian.
London, Simpkin, Marshall and Co., Calcutta, Thacker & Spink, 1853.

8vo, half title, pictorial lithographed title, lithographed map of the island of Java uncoloured, and 23 tinted lithographed plates, all coloured, original brown pictorial cloth gilt.
Abbey Travel 556; Bastin & Brommer 406 n.

Plates include views of Batavia, Penang and Singapore, Charles Kinloch visited Penang, Singapore and Java in 1852, returning to Calcutta in October of that year. The plates by W. Spreat of Exeter are considered poor. Apart from those sketches which were presented to him during his journey, the plates were after his own drawings. The views of Singapore include the West Side of Government Hill, and Penang Hill, several are of Boro Bodor and its Temple. As well as architecture, plates also show natural history, plates of tea and coffee plants and a nutmeg on the tree, and also costume plates. No. 16 is reproduced on Plate XXVIII.

297

LA PLACE, Cyrille-Pierre-Theodore.

Voyage Autour du Monde par les Mers de l'Inde et de Chine executee sur la Corvette de l'Etat la Favourite pendant les Annees 1830, 1831, 1832 sous le Commandment de La Place.

Atlas Historique. 2 vols., folio, 72 handcoloured aquatints, contemporary half polished calf gilt with red and green morocco labels on spine.
Atlas Hydrographique, 5 vols., 8vo, 12 large charts on 11 sheets.
Hill I, p. 175; Sabin 38985; Ferguson 1669.

Early view of Sydney, the plates have held colours well, a brilliant set including many of types, occupations and trades of China and also Dutch East Indies, and Java. The purpose of the voyage was to show the French flag in eastern and other waters, in order to re-establish French influence over Indo-China and the Pacific. The voyage was also very successful scientifically. The hydrographic work was thorough and reliable, the work done in the Anamba and Natuna groups of Malaysia was valuable, and a good collection of natural history specimens was brought back. La Place visited Singapore, Manila, Canton, Batavia, Chile, and other ports.

297

297

Paris del.

297

246 THE EXOTIC AND THE BEAUTIFUL

Hunely sc.

MCLEOD, John.

Narrative for a Voyage, in His Majesty's Late Ship Alceste, to the Yellow Sea, along the Coast of Corea, and through its Numerous Hitherto Undiscovered Islands, to the Island of Lewchew; with an Account of her Shipwreck in the Straits of Gaspar.
London, John Murray, 1817.

First edition. 8vo, engraved uncoloured portrait by T. Wageman, 4 handcoloured aquatint plates, contemporary boards, paper label on spine.
Chaplin, p. 99; Cordier, cols. 2107-8; Lipperheide, No. 1529; Prideaux, pp. 251 (the first edition); Abbey 559 cites second edition; not in Tooley.

The second edition of 1818 carries an additional plate (No. 6 with I. M'Leod delin.). A third edition appeared in 1819 and a fourth in 1820. This voyage was undertaken while Lord Amherst's Embassy, was in China. Lord Amherst was on board the Alceste, making the return journey, when she was wrecked, but he and all the crew survived. See also Captain Basil Hall's and Henry Ellis's accounts.

MOORE, Lieut. Joseph [and Captain Frederick Marryat].

Eighteen Views taken at and near Rangoon [Views ...in the Birman Empire].
London, Thomas Clay, [1825-1826].

First and second series bound in one vol., oblong folio, engraved allegorical title incorporating the dedication, engraved subscription list with mezzotint vignette by J. Bromley after T. Stothard, 24 fine handcoloured aquatint views after J. Moore and F. Marryat, lithographed map of Rangoon by W. Day, contemporary half red morocco, red morocco label on upper cover, modern endpapers, blue cloth porfolio, without wrappers and lithographed leaves of subscribers, text series 1 without title and to subscribers leaves. With text and plan of Rangoon. The text, which is a smaller format, is bound interleaved with the plates, the 24 views comprise 18 from the first series and 6 from the second series. Plates 7 and 8 are marked Proof. Plate 16 in second state with word adjacent corrected.
Abbey Travel 404; Tooley (1954) 334.

Text rarely found to accompany this beautiful set of plates of Rangoon, many showing the British Military in evidence or on duty against the buildings and temples of the city.

OVERMEER FISSCHER, Johan Frederick van.
Bijdrage tot de kennits van het Japanische Rijk door J.F. van Overmeer Fisscher, Ambtenaar van Neerlandsch Indie, laatst in Japan. Met platen.
Amsterdam, J. Miller & Co., C.A. Spin, 1833.

4to, French title, title-page, contents, 320pp. text, 15 finely coloured lithographed plates, contemporary Dutch dark blue calf gilt by J.H. Peters of Amsterdam, elaborately tooled in gilt and blind with overall design incorporating Western and Japanese symbols, original printed wrappers bound in, binder's ticket on rear pastedown, preserved in modern tan cloth box.
From the library of Eugenie and Jean Furstenberg. Alt Japan Kat. 1098; Cordier 489-90; Landwehr 385.

The author spent nine years in Decima after his arrival in Japan in 1822.

PERELAER, M.T.H.; REES, W.A. van.
Nederlansch-Indie.
Leiden, Sitjhoff, 1881-1883.

First edition. 4 vols., small folio, lithographed titles, 103 chromolithographed plates, mounted on heavy paper after drawings by Jhr. J.C. Rappard, original red morocco backed embossed red cloth.
Bastin & Bromer 687 & 688.

Rare complete set consisting of Batavia, Java, Buitzorg and other possessions. The work represents a romanticised account of the country and enjoyed considerable popularity despite its high price. This beautiful production is distinguished in the history of Indonesian illustration because the lithographs were produced from original photographs and not drawings. The text, by two of Indonesia's most popular writers, is considered highly readable.

301

301

Ein chinesischer Klontong (Hausirer) mit seinem Kulie.

302

PERRY, Commodore Matthew C. [and] HAWKS, Francis I.
Narrative of the Expedition of an American Squadron to the China Seas and Japan. Performed in the Years 1852, 1853 and 1854 Under the Command of Commodore M.C. Perry, United States Navy. By Order of the Government of the United States.
New York, D. Appleton and Company, 1856.

4to, 74 mostly tinted lithographed plates, 11 folding lithographed maps, other woodcut illustrations in the text, original cloth gilt.

This report of the important first expedition to Japan for four centuries and preliminary attempts to establish relations between the two countries. A tour de force of diplomacy on the part of Commodore Perry and his American expeditionary force.

303

PFYFFER ZU NEUECK, Joseph Jacob Xavier.
Skizzen von der Insel Java and derselben verschiedenen Behwohnern.
Schaffhausen, Franz Herter, 1829 [1832].

First edition. 4to, lithographed additional title, 15 finely handcoloured lithographed plates by Franz Hurter and others, heightened with gum Arabic, folding lithographed map of Java, 4pp., introduction, text (pp.[1]-92), descriptive list of the plates separately paginated (pp.[1]-11). Unpaginated leaf bound within plates "Javan'sches alphabet" (recto) and "Javan'sche zahlen" (verso).
Bastin & Brommer 186 (&c.); not in Abbey or Longchamp.

A rare work on the Indonesian island of Java, covering the geography, topography, costumes, natural history, music, geology, religion and language of the Javanese people.

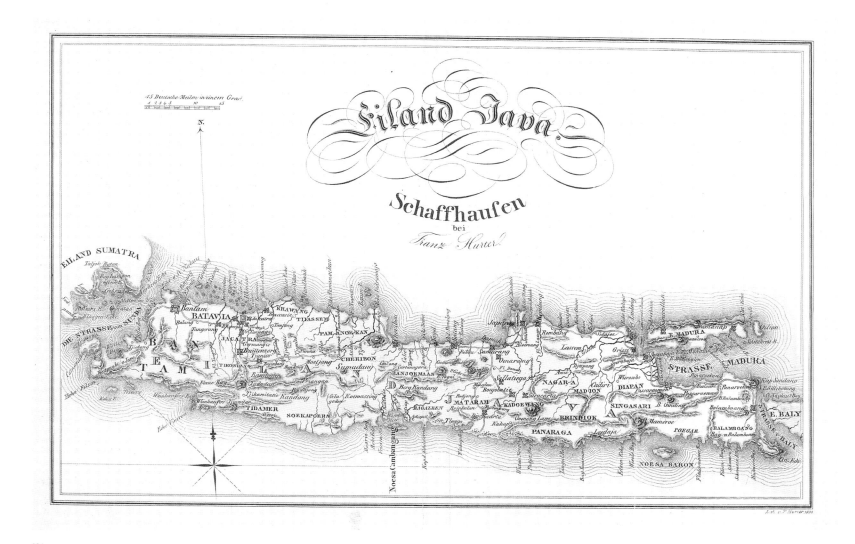

304

RAFFLES, Sir Thomas Stamford Bingley.
The History of Java.
London, Printed for Black, Parbury, and Allen, Booksellers to the Hon. East-India Company [and] John Murray,1817.

2 vols., 4to, dedication, preface, introduction xix to xlviii; text pp. 1-479, Vol. II with similar collation, text pp. 1-291, errata for both vols. in Vol. II, publishers' advertisement with notice advising that the plates would be executed principally by Mr W. Daniell, folding map of Java coloured in outline, and a total of 66 plates, these a mixture of handcoloured aquatint plates, uncoloured soft ground etching, uncoloured line, uncoloured line and aquatint, in addition there are engraved vignettes on pp. 1, 11, 16, 20, 51, 54, 63, contemporary black morocco. Abbey Travel 254; Tooley 103; Prideaux pp. 252-3; 348.

A second edition of Raffles' work was published by Murray in 1830, 2 vols., 8vo and with a separate 4to atlas and was remaindered by Bohn. It seems likely from the Prospectus that all the unsigned plates might be by William Daniell, but in all probability only the ten excellent handcoloured aquatint costume plates are his. He did make a point of not signing plates engraved by him after other artists which is presumably the case here and this is remarked with regard to another work by him in this catalogue. Raffles, who was

himself a Governor of Java, is said to have completed the History in seven months. He was knighted by the Prince Regent in 1817 after the publication of this work.
Bound with EDY, John William. Boydell's Picturesque Scenery of Norway. Lodon, Hurst, Robinson, and Co., Boydell and Co., 1820. Folio, 2 vols. in one, 80 handcoloured aquatint plates. Abbey Travel 254 (described in full in Vol. II).

305

SALM, Abraham and GREIVE, Johan Conrad. Jr.
Java. Na Schilderijen en Teekeningen.
Amsterdam, Frans Buffa & Zonen [c. 1872].

Folio, 24 handcoloured lithographed plates by Greive after A. Salm, mounted on card, preserved in brown cloth portfolio.
Bastin & Brommer Note 659; Landwehr 421.

"One of Buffa's most beautiful publications", (Landwehr). Salm, a self-taught artist from Amsterdam, lived in Indonesia for 29 years and painted numerous landscapes, mostly of Java. He chose these 24 sketches to illustrate this work. The views were printed from three plates and finished by hand.

308

308

SILVER, Jacob Mortimer Wier.

Sketches of Japanese Manners and Customs.
London, Day & Son Ltd, 1867.

2 vols., 4to, chromolithographed title, 3ll., 51pp with 18 woodcut vignettes, steel and 27 chromolithographed plates, after traditional drawings by a local Japanese artist, contemporary half calf gilt ruled over original cloth, g.e.
Lipperheide 1562; not in Abbey Travel.

The traditional Japanese illustrations in this work are extremely beautiful.

307

SMITH, Captain.

Asiatic Costumes, a Series of forty-four coloured engravings from designs taken from life by Captain Smith, 44th Regiment with a description to each subject.
London, R. Ackermann, 1828.

First edition. 8vo, printed title, engraved coloured frontispiece, [1] leaf, dedication to the Duke of York, 88 pp., 6 engraved and coloured plans, 54 handcoloured aquatint plates by J.C. Stadler, no. 1-54, half straight grained morocco over marbled paper.
Not in Tooley or Abbey; Brunet II, 324; Vinet 2195; Colas.

An attractive set of costume plates.

SNOW, William R.

Sketches in Chinese Life and Character, [c. 1860].

Three original parts in one vol., [all published], folio, 18 handcoloured lithographed plates, of life in China by William R. Snow, plates indicate slightly humorous approach by the artist. China half black morocco.
Not in Abbey, Tooley, Colas, Lipperheide, or Cordier.

An apparently scarce set of plates including Costermongers in Victoria Street, Hong Kong; Going for a Picnic; Close Shave; Caravans (camels in front in foreground, railway train in distance); Group of Coolies at a portable Soup Kitchen.

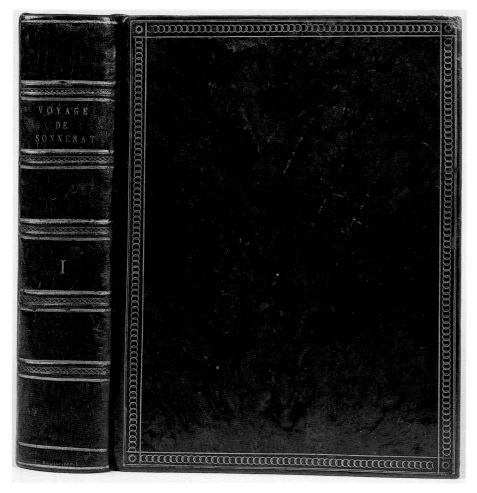

309

309

SONNERAT, Pierre.
Voyage aux Indes Orientales et la Chine, fait par l'Ordre du Roi, depuis 1774 jusqu'en 1781, dans lequel on traite du Moeurs, de la Religion, des Sciences & des Arts des Indiens, des Chinois, des Pegouins & des Madegasses, suivi d'Observations sur le Cap de Bonne Esperance, les Iles de France & de Bourbon, les Maldives...
Paris, Chez l'Auteur, 1782.

First edition, 2 vols., 4to, 140 handcoloured aquatint plates, all but one handcoloured, many folding, contemporary green tree calf, sides gilt bordered, spine gilt in compartments, g.e.
Cordier Sinica III, 2102; Boucher de la Richardiere V, 268.

This work is a celebrated classic of natural history exploration and discovery in the Far East. Extremely rare to find these beautiful engraved plates handcoloured as here. Sonnerat was the son of French Intendant of Mauritius. Prior to this voyage he had been on an expedition to the Philippines and Molucca, the account being published in 1776. He then made a second voyage via the Maldives, Ceylon, the Philippines, China, Burma, Madagascar and the Cape of Good Hope, of which this is the account. This treats of all aspect of life particularly in China.

STAUNTON, Sir George.

An Authentic Account of an Embassy from the King of Great Britain to the Emperor of China.
London, W. Bulmer, 1787-1796.

3 vols. including atlas of plates, 2 vols., 4to text with frontispiece portraits, and folio atlas of plates, large engraved folding map and 43 copper engraved maps and plates, some maps double-page, two copper engraved frontispieces, portraits accompanying text, text half calf and plate volume full calf.
Cox I, 344.

In 1792 Staunton accompanied his father to China in the capacity of page to the Ambassador. He became proficient in Chinese and on arriving at the Court of the Emperor, was the only Englishman able to converse. On his return to London he wrote this text to accompany his drawings made on the Embassy. He was later to join the East India Company as writer and expert in Chinese matters. "The account of this famous embassy was prepared at Government expense. Apart from its Chinese importance, it is of considerable interest owing to the description of the various places en route which were visited, including Madeira, Teneriffe, Rio de Janeiro, St. Helena, Tristan d'Acunha, Amsterdam Island, Java, Sumatra, Cochin-China etc. Britain was anxious to establish formal diplomatic relations with China and thus open the way for unimpeded trade relations. But the pall of Chinese reserve and self-sufficiency, which for many centuries seldom admitted penetration, still hung over this empire and effectually resisted Lord Macartney's arguments and gifts. His visit gave us a most interesting account of Chinese manners and customs at the close of the 18th century." (Cox I, 344.)

TITSINGH, Isaac.

Illustrations of Japan; consisting of private memoirs and anecdotes of the reigning dynasty of the Djogouns, or Sovereigns of Japan; a description of the Feasts and Ceremonies observed throughout the year at their court; and of the ceremonies customary at marriages and funerals, to which are subjoined, observations on the legal suicide of the Japanese, remarks on their poetry, and explanation of their mode of reckoning time, particulars respecting the dosia powder...
London, William Clowes for R. Ackermann, 1822.

4to, 13 plates of which plates no. 1 and 4 coloured line; nos. 2 & 3, coloured aquatints; no 13 coloured line-and-stipple, this plate is folding, and comprises six plates joined, making two parallel panoramic strips; the remainder coloured line with a little aquatinting, the final plate no. later 19th century calf, sides panelled gilt.
Cordier Bibliotheca Japonica p. 450; Martin Hardie pp. 113-114, 313; Prideaux pp. 128, 351, 375; Tooley (1954), 489; Abbey Travel 557.

Isaac Titsingh for 14 years served the Dutch East India Company as chief of their settlement at Nagasaki. He is claimed by Mr E.F. Strange in his "Japanese Illustration" as the earliest European collector of Japanese prints.

310

312

313

312

VAN PERS, A.
Nederlandsch Oost-Indische Typen.
The Hague, C.W. Mieling, 1854.

Folio, 56 coloured lithographed plates, loose as issued, most
after Van Pers, and lithographed by C.W. Mieling.
Not in Abbey; Bastin & Bromer 497 for list of plates.

Many of the plates are of Chinese life, characters and
costume, but also of Java and its inhabitants, cultivating
rice, flying a kite, opium smokers, also warriors in Borneo.
Van Pers was born in Doornik and after enlisting in the
army, sailed for Indonesia. In 1839 he was appointed
engraver and draughtsman in the Geographical Department
of the Bureau of Statistics in the General Secretariat,
Buitenzorg. Four years later he moved to the recently
established printing office of the Topograical Bureau of the
Engineers. While there he provided lithographed
illustrations for Junghuhn and at this time he was taken on
by the booksellers Ukena & Co., Batavia, to work with
Ernest Hardouin on this particular project. In 1851 Lange
& Co., Batavia published Part 1 of the work with plates by
M. Degens, the printer at the Lithographic Establishment of
the Engineers. The work was soon abandoned as Van Pers
had to leave Indonesia due to ill health.

313

WATHEN, James.
Journal of a Voyage in 1811 and 1812, to Madras and China…
London, for J. Nichols, Son, and Bentley, 1814.

4to, 24 handcoloured aquatint plates, signed I. Wathen delt
and I. Clark dirext, published by Black, Parry & Co. and
Nichols & Co., contemporary half calf, over marbled boards.
Abbey Travel 517; Cordier col. 2107; Gay, No. 1063;
Mendelssohn, Vol. II, pg. 591; Prideaux, pp. 237, 355.

These attractive plates include the Great Pagoda, at
Congeveram; Mallacca, with the Hope at Anchor in the
Roads; Anson's Bay, from within the Bocca Tigris; China
Street, with part of the European Factories, Canton; View of
the Bocca Tigris from under the 2nd Bar Pagoda; James
Town, St. Helena, looking to Ladder Hill Barracks.

314

WRIGHT, Thomas.
China in a Series of Views…
London, 1843.

4 vols. in two, 4to, 128 steel engraved plates by Thomas
Allom, original half calf and embossed cloth.

315

Pacific including Antipodes

315
ANGAS, George French.
South Australia Illustrated.
London, Thomas M'Lean, 1847.

First edition. Folio, 2pp. list of subscribers, hand-tinted list of subscribers, lithographed dedication to Queen Adelaide, 60 handcoloured tinted lithographed plates, (58 after Angas, 2 after T.S. Gill, lithographed by Angas, J.W. Giles, W. Hawkins, William Wing and two unsigned), half calf gilt.
Abbey Travel II, 577; Tooley 62-63; Colas 133.

An important visual record. In the preface Angas states, "With the hope of preserving true and life-like records of men and scenes, so quickly passing away, I have endeavoured…to describe the most interesting and peculiar features of South Australia and its Aboriginal inhabitants." He described how he visited all the parts of the Colony making himself conversant with the manners and habits of native tribes, whose existence is unknown to the world.

316
ANGAS, George French.
The New Zealanders Illustrated.
London, Thomas M'Lean, 1847.

Folio, 2 pp. subscription list, handcoloured additional title, 60 handcoloured tinted lithographed plates after Angas, lithographed by Angas, W. Hawkins, Louisa Hawkins and J.W. Giles, later red morocco over red cloth.
Abbey Travel 589; Tooley 61.

Again Angas states that he visited both islands in order to learn as much as possible about the Maoris and the changes that were going on in their social and physical condition, so that people in England should have a better idea of them. He also penetrated through the interior. He said he had succeeded in getting portraits of the most important chiefs and their families, making sketches on the spot.

ANGAS, George French.
Description of the Barossa Range and its
Neighbourhood, in South Australia.
London, Smith, Elder, 1849.

First edition. Folio, 6 handcoloured lithographed plates, by and
after Angas, printed by M & N. Hanrart, two lithographed
maps, one folding, original printed wrappers.
Abbey Travel 580; Ferguson 4986; Wantrup, Australian Rare
books 1788-1900, 238

A scarce work. Appeared in Keynes I at Christie's as the first
copy seen at auction for 25 years. Interesting because so
much of Angas's work was reinterpreted by English
lithographers but this book is particularly desirable because
Angas interpreted his own work offering a more accurately
observed look at Australian scenery. The folding lithographed
map of the country shows the seven special surveys.

Summer-Hill Creek below Lewis Ponds.　　　　　　　　Gold Washing.

318

318

ANGUS [ANGAS], George French.
Views of the Gold Regions of Australia.
London, J. Hogarth, Hullmandel & Walton, 1851.

Folio, pp. 1& 2 description of the plates, 5 handcoloured lithographed plates, plus lithographed title, signed on the plate surface of plate 3, F.W. Hulme, Lith. Hullmandel & Walton's Process, the latter off the plate surface at foot.
Ferguson 5997 (for plain copy) and 5998; Abbey Travel 583.

This work was evidently copies from the book published in Sydney in the same year, Six Views of the Gold Fields of Ophir, No. 582. (See below). The fact that the name of the artist has been mistakenly given as Angus suggests that this London version was published without Angas's knowledge. There is no plate corresponding to Plate 5 of the Sydney edition, No. 582. These plates show gold washing at Summer-Hill Creek; Ophir Diggings, Summer Hill Creeks; Gold washing/ Fitz Roy Bar. Ophir Diggings 1851; Ophir, Summer Hill Creek, from above the junction of Lewis' Ponds; Ophir, at the junction June 1851.

　Angas the son of George Fife Angas, one of the founders of South Australia. He studied anatomical drawing and lithography in London after having at first been placed in business, which he disliked. He visited Malta and Sicily in 1841, and published his first book of travels in 1842. He went to Australia in 1843 and later spent about a year in South Africa. This collection has all Angas's great works.

319

ANGAS, George French.
Six Views of the Gold Field of Ophir, at Summerhill and Lewis's Ponds Creeks.
Sydney, Woolcott and Clarke, Kemp & Fairfax Printers, 1851.

First edition. Oblong folio, 6 handcoloured lithographed plates signed on plate surface G.F. Angas, one printed leaf (contents).
Abbey Travel 582.

This Sydney edition was the first edition.

320

**BARRAUD, Charles Decimus
[and] TRAVERS W.T.L., editor.**
New Zealand Graphic and Descriptive.
London, Sampson Low & Co., 1877.

Folio, viii, 40pp., 24 mounted coloured lithographed plates, plus title and 6 uncoloured lithographed plates, 31 woodcuts in text, modern half calf over original cloth.
Bagnall New Zealand National Bibliography 320; Hocken 303.

Views selected from the provincial districts, with descriptions.

320

324

BARRINGTON, George.
The History of New South Wales including Botany Bay,
Port Jackson, Pamarata, Sydney…
London, W. Flint for J. Jones, 1802.

First edition, first issue. 8vo, half title, directions to the binder at
the end, engraved handcloured vignette title, 15 handcoloured
engraved plates, full page woodengraved illustration.
Ferguson I, 345; Abbey II, 565; Tooley 80; Whittell 39; Wood
p. 222.

Wantrup stated that this work was almost certainly not by
Barrington, who had suffered from ill health from 1800
until his death in 1804. Wantrup considered that both this
work and An Account of a Voyage to New South Wales were
taken more or less verbatim from David Collins's two vol.,
Account of the English Colony in New South Wales.

**BOUGAINVILLE, Louis Yves Philippe Potentien,
Baron de.**
Album pittoresque de la fregate la Thetis et de la corvette
l'Esperance. Collection de dessins relatifs a leur voyage
autour du monde en 1824, 1825 et 1826, sous les ordres
de M. le baron de Bougainville…recueillis et publies par
M. le vicomte de La Touanne… Paris, Bulla, 1827.

Folio, 44pp., title vignette, 28 engraved handcoloured plates,
original wrappers preserved in modern morocco backed cloth
covered box. Hill 161.

This fine series of views was issued separately nine years
before the official account of Hyacinthe de Bougainville's
voyage was published. The voyage of the Boudeuse and the
Etoile under Bougainville became the first official French
circumnavigation. Louis de Bougainville had been an aide
de camp to the Marquis de Montcalm in Canada, and he
acted for the French at their surrender to the British at
Montreal in 1760. He attempted to colonise the Iles
Malouines in 1762-64, seeing their strategic advantage in
commanding the route to the Pacific around South
America. Diplomatic negotiations in Paris later forced

Bougainville to cede the islands, (known as Islas Malvinas,
to the Spanish and as the Falkland Islands to the English)
to Spain. Bougainville visited Rio de Janeiro, Montevideo,
Patagonia in South America, Buenos Aires, when order for
the expulsion of the Jesuits arrived, then proceeded
through the Strait of Magellan and across the Pacific,
visiting the Tuamotu Archipelago, Tahiti, the Samoa Islands,
the New Hebrides, and the Solomon, Louisiade, the New
Britain archipelagos.

CHEVALIER, Nicolas. N.
Chevalier's Album of Chromolithographs.
Melbourne, Charles Troedel, [1865].

First edition. Folio, 12 chromolithographed plates
Ferguson 17429; Wanthrup 256.

Wantrup claims that no library of books on Australia is
complete without this work. Comprises some of
Chevalier's best work, drawn on treks through the
Victorian bush. Has been described as the first example of
reproduction of High Victorian taste in landscape art, by a
famous exponent of Australian Colonial Romantic Art.
Chevalier had also pioneered a new technique in book
production. (Sometimes catalogued under publisher
Troedel's name as The Melbourne Album.)

EARLE, Augustus.
Sketches Illustrative of the Native Inhabitants and
Islands of New Zealand.
London, Robert Martin, A.R. Spottiswoode, 1838.

First edition. Oblong folio, 1 leaf description of the plates, 10
handcoloured lithographed plates, the plates with an imprint only
where there are two images to a plate, i.e. plates 1 and 5.
Abbey Travel 587.

The Image of "Herald, or Peace-Maker" is repeated twice
on the plates with double image.

Südsee-Erinnerungen

(1875—1880)

von

Franz Hernsheim

ehem. Consul des Deutschen Reiches auf Jaluit.

Mit einem einleitenden Vorwort

von

Dr. Otto Finsch.

BERLIN.

A. Hofmann & Comp.

GRASSET DE SAINT-SAUVEUR, Jacques.
Voyage Pittoresques dans les quatre Paties du Monde, ou troisieme Edition de l'Encyclopedie des Voyages. Contenant les Costumes des principaux peuples de l'Europe, de l'Asie, de l'Afrique, de l'Amerique, et des sauvages de la mer du sud, graves et colories avec soin, accompagnes de six cartes geographiques; suivis d'un précis historique sur les moeurs de chaque people.
Paris, chez Madame veuve Hocquart, 1806.

2 vols, 8vo, 160 handcoloured engraved plates, 6 folding engraved maps, plates by Mirelle after Saint-Sauveur, contemporary half calf.
Colas 1302.

It seems that Saint-Sauveur felt that the plates of the Pacific were the most attractive and exotic.

GULLY, JOHN and HAAST, Julius von.
New Zealand Scenery Chromolithographed after original watercolour drawings.
London, Ward, 1877.

First edition. Large folio, 15 chromolithographed plates mounted on card as issued, descriptive letterpress, original green pebbled cloth, gilt lettered direct on upper cover, g.e.
Hocken p. 305.

Striking series of views illustrating some of the dramatic scenery in fact recently featured in the film, "The Lord of the Rings". "Mr Gully, the artist, ranks as one of the most accomplished artists New Zealand produced." (Hocken).

HERNSHELM, Franz [and] FINSCH, Dr. Otto.
Sudsee-Erinnerungen (1875-1880)
Berlin, A. Hoffmann [1883]

4to, vignette title, 13 chromolithographed plates, three quarter calf and red pebbled cloth gilt.

An apparently scarce work, not to be found in any of the relevant bibliographies, nor on ABPC or Deutsches Jahrbuch.

LYCETT, J.
Views in Australia or New South Wales, & Van Diemen's Land delineated...
London, J. Souter, 1824-25.

Oblong folio, dedication, advertisement, pp. I & ii, Descriptive text, 48 ll., one leaf per plate, 49 handcoloured aquatint plates, except No. 1 (title), which is a coloured lithograph, two maps of New South Wales and Van Diemens Land, second coloured, half green calf over original boards, preserved in green cloth box.
Abbey Travel 570; Tooley 310; Ferguson, nos. 974 (parts), 1031 (volume).

A twelfth part, which the Advertisement says was to contain a brief History of Australia, does not seem to have been published. Also apparently never published was a Natural History of Australia, which, it is mentioned, was to appear in the same format.

"The aquatints according to Maggs appear to follow Lycett's original drawings more closely than do the lithographs..." (Abbey). Aquatint was in its heyday at this time and its superior brilliance and definition would be obvious and familiar to the purchaser of an ambitious coloured-page book such as this.

329

329

MANN, D. D.

The Present Picture of New South Wales, illustrated with four large coloured views, from drawings taken on the spot, of Sydney, the seat of government; with a Plan of the Colony, taken from actual survey by public authority. London, John Booth, 1811.

4to (text), a new plan of the Settlements in New South Wales, coloured and folding, 4 folio plates, all handcoloured aquatints, preserved in linen box.
Abbey Travel 566.

The plates are signed J. Eyre del; Clark sculp., all four views of Sydney. They are probably the earliest authentic coloured views of any Australian town, and certainly the earliest aquatints. The man from whose drawings they were engraved, J. Eyre, was one of the early convicts. Complete with the plates, this book is very rare, and the text or the plates alone almost equally so.

OLIVER, COMMANDER Richard Aldworth.
A Series of Lithographic Drawings from Sketches in New Zealand.
London, Dickinson Brothers, [1852].

Large folio, title and text, descriptive of plates, one leaf, verso blank, 9 handcoloured lithographed plates, original cloth-backed wrappers, letterpress titling on upper cover, preserved in modern cloth portfolio.
Abbey Travel 592; Hocken p. 167; Tooley 349.

The subscription list cannot have increased since no more parts seem to have been published. Plates are signed Dickinson & Co. lith. and Capt. Oliver delt, except No. 7 which is signed, R.A. Clive delt. Plates are of local types, from a New Zealand chief to Harry Bluff and Johnny. The signature R.A. Clive seems to have been a misreading or the result of a defect on the stone.

331
SHIPLEY, Conway.
Sketches in the Pacific. The South Sea Islands.
London, T. McLean, 1851.

Folio, handcoloured lithographic title-page, a plate of facsimile signatures and 25 lithograph plates, 14 of them handcoloured; an excellent copy in the original blue cloth, red cloth titling inlay at centre of cover with complex gilt borders; red cloth spine neatly repaired.
Abbey, 601; Ferguson, 15656A; Hill (2nd ed.), 1564; Kroepelien, 1189; O'Reilly-Reitman, 1125.

Shipley's delightful and celebrated collection of Pacific views. A beautiful copy of one of the great illustrated books of the South Pacific, and a very scarce book today. Shipley's series of wonderful evocations of the romantic islands of the South Pacific, 'drawn from nature and on Stone' by the artist himself, is one of the hardest Pacific voyage books to find.

This copy has an original letter from the author tipped-in at the start, in which Shipley discusses the plates for the book at some length, and the incorrect order in which they have been bound in his correspondent's copy. Shipley lists the plates in their correct order and provides a small sketch to identify one of the images.

Shipley sailed from Valparaiso on the Calypso in February 1848. During the next few months he visited Pitcairn, Tahiti, Samoa and Fiji. He describes and illustrates each of the four locations, with lithographs of a haunting beauty, evoking a world of paradise islands. The three views of Pitcairn's Island are really the best that survive from the earlier years of settlement; Shipley gives a good textual account too of the way of life still practised on the most remote of all island settlements.

In the Tahitian section, several fine views of Papeete Bay show shipping at anchor, and frequently the Calypso appears in these views to lend scale. There is a fine image of the ship beating to windward after leaving Bora Bora.

The National Union Catalog records only the Library of Congress copy of this surprisingly rare book, while Ferguson notes only the copy in the National Library of Australia.

332
SKOGMAN, C.
FREGATTEN Eugenies Resa Omkring Jorden.
Stockholm, C.A. Virgin, [1854-55].

2 vols, 8vo, 20 coloured lithographed plates, three folding tinted maps, 6 full-page engravings, 18 engravings in text.
Hill 573; Judd 163; and p.41.

This is the official account of the first Swedish circumnavigation, on the Eugenie, under the command of Captain Christian Adolf Virgin. Skogman, the author of the account, was from a prominent family, graduated from the University at Uppsala, and became a naval officer in 1839. He was the official astronomer for the voyage, which lasted from 1851-53, visiting the East and West Coasts of South America and Pacific and Indian ocean islands. After the Galapagos, Honolulu, San Francisco, Tahiti, the Cook Islands, Samoa, Tonga, Fiji, Sydney and Port Jackson, Seringapatam Shoal, Guam, Hong Kong, Canton, Manila, Singapore, and Batavia were visited. The expedition was greeted on their return to Stockholm by King Oscar I. The expedition naturalist, Nils Johan Andersson, was the first Darwinian botanist in Sweden. Skogman's account is particularly prized for its fine colour plates. (Hill).

333
WAHLEN, Auguste.
Moeurs, Usages et Costumes et tous les Peuples du Monde. D'apres les documents authentiques et les voyages les plus recents...
Brussells, a la librairie historique – artistique, 1843-44.

4 vols, large 8vo, 211 woodengraved handcoloured plates, by Doms, Duverger, Lisbet, Markaert, Mercier, Pannemaker, Vermorcken etc.
Colas 3041; Lipperheide 61; Vinet 2124.

Wahlen was the pseudonym for Jean-Francois-Nicolas Loumyer (cf. Querard III, 990). Vol. I, Asia; Vol. II, Pacifica; Vol. III, Africa & America; Vol. IV, Europe.
Brunet III, 1789 quotes an anonymous edition dated 1842-47, a compilation of the same kind.

332

332

334

WAKEFIELD, Edward Jerningham.

Adventure in New Zealand from 1839-1844; with some Account of the beginning of the British Colonization of the Islands.

London, William Clowes & Sons for John Murray, 1845.

First edition. 2 vols, 8vo, folding map, original green cloth. Hocken p. 124; Hill 1811.

At the age of 19, the author went to New Zealand with the first settlers in the Tory. His account is an important early social history of the settlements of Wellington, New Plymouth, Wanganui, and Nelson. Based on his diary and letters sent back to England, it is full of minute incidents and the details of daily life, covering such groups and individuals as whalers, natives, explorers, missionaries, settlers, and the government (Hill).

This work serves as a companion volume to the following item Wakefield's Illustrations to Adventures...

334

WEBBER, James.

View in the South Seas, from Drawings by the late James Webber, draftsman on board the Resolution, Captain James Cooke [sic], from the year 1776 to 1780. With letterpress, descriptive of the various scenery, &c. These plates form a new series, and are of the same size as those engraved for Captain Cooke's last voyage. The drawings are in the possession of the Board of Admiralty.
London, Boydell & Co., Printed by W. Bulmer and Co., 1808. [but c. 1820].

Folio, 1 p.l., 16 handcoloured aquatint plates, plate 2 bound as frontispiece, with imprint on plates April 1.1809 by Boydell & Compy. No. 90, Cheapside.
Abbey Travel 595; Tooley 501.

Webber created 16 Pacific and East Indies views between 1788 and 1792; these were republished posthumously by Boydell as Views in the South Seas. In this work Webber's coloured aquatint views are accompanied by a text consisting of quotations, mainly from the official account of Cook's Third Voyage. The anonymous editor of these extracts was probably James Burney. The title page is dated 1808 in all copies, but the plate imprints are dated April, 1809, and the watermark dates vary widely from copy to copy. Webber had been trained as an artist in Berne and Paris, then returning to London. He produced a remarkable body of work to illustrate Cook's third voyage and supervised the engraving. These plates include Queen Charlotte's Sound, New Zealand, and on via the Friendly Islands, Otahaite, Cracatoa, Waheiadooa, Taloo, Kamtchatka to Macao, including the residence of Camoens, when he wrote his Lusiad, and finally Cracatoa again.

WAKEFIELD, Edward Jerningham.

Illustrations to Adventures in New Zealand, by Edward Jerningham Wakefield... lithographed from original drawings taken on the spot by Mrs. Wickstted – Mill King – Mrs. Fox – Mr. John Saxton – Mr. Charles Heaphy – Mr S.C. Brees and Captain W Mein Smith.
London, Smith, Elder & Co., 1845.

First edition. Oblong folio, handcoloured vignette title, 20 handcoloured lithographed plates on thin card, comprising 5 folding panoramas on joined sheets, 10 plates printed two to a sheet, 5 printed on single sheets, quarter red calf, over moiré cloth.
Ellis, Early Prints of New Zealand 342-361; Abbey Travel 588; Hocken p. 21.

These plates accompany Wakefield's text. The reason for the publication of the atlas by Smith, Elder, rather than by Murray, is not clear.

WILLIAMSON, Thomas.

Foreign Field Sports, Fisheries, Sporting Anecdotes...
With a Supplement of New South Wales.
London, H.R. Young, J. M'Creery, 1819.

Second edition. Folio, title, index, 110 plates, all but two handcoloured aquatints, Nos. 21 and 43, coloured line, and No. 8 coloured line and stipple, contemporary calf.
Abbey Travel 3; Tooley 275: Prideaux p. 375; Schwerdt I, p. 179; Martin Hardie p. 137.

The plates are the same as in the first edition, except the order in this edition has been slightly changed, the type face is slightly different, but accords line by line with first edition. There is no separate title for the New South Wales section. Williamson also wrote the text for the Oriental Field Sports, see elsewhere in this catalogue. Plates include hunting of crocodile, buffalo, zebra, gt. boa and tiger, elephant, wild boar, rhinoceros, fishing in Lapland, hunting the elk; bull fighting, whale fishing, kangaroo, opossum and also shows warriors of New South Wales.